LIFE FROM THE LAND

LIFE FROM THE LAND

*The Growth of Farming
in Western Europe*

ROBERT TROW-SMITH

LONGMANS

Longmans, Green & Co Ltd
48 Grosvenor Street London W1

*And associated companies, branches and representatives
throughout the world*

© Robert Trow-Smith 1967
First published 1967

Printed in Great Britain by
Ebenezer Baylis and Son Ltd
The Trinity Press, Worcester, and London

Contents

Illustrations

CHAPTER ONE

The Beginning

Man as an animal needs food. Man as a tool-using hominoid has the means with which to produce food, and not merely accept what nature happens to offer. Man as a thinking being has the mental power to extend, to intensify, to perfect the control of his environment and his production of food to the stage where farming need occupy a few men in every hundred; and his non-farming fellows are freed to develop their brand of civilization. Nevertheless, that civilization is based upon the inescapable business of farming; and in Western Europe and over much of the rest of the world agriculture has shaped the face of the countryside, conditioned many of our mental attitudes, started wars and imposed peace. It provides one of those necessities—air, water and food—without which life ends. In the absence of the farmer—be he Argentinian cattleman, New Zealand pastoralist, Caucasian ploughman—the flat-dweller in Stevenage New Town or Montparnasse or Dusseldorf dies of starvation within the month. Agriculture, in short, is more than a way of life, an occupation for profit, an aberrant pantheism: it is an industry which is basic to human existence.

Farming began as all great inventions begin: by men applying their brains and their hands to a problem. The problem was a product of natural causes.

Climate, which has always been the absolute dictator of agricultural practice, was the only begetter of agriculture itself; or so the current view runs. The farmer can grow only what crops and stock his weather permits him to grow. It was said, long ago, that it is technically possible to grow bananas on the summit of Snowdon or the Matterhorn, given the resources to create the correct microclimate. And so it is. But in practice the banana requires certain natural minimums of temperature and sunshine; oats will only ripen up to a given degree of latitude; a cow will not thrive in an excess of heat; and arctic conditions inhibit all farming. Throughout the ten thousand years since agriculture began, it has always been vulnerable to changes in climate. By one of the major and most consequential quirks in history it was almost certainly an onslaught of aridity which forced the hunter and the nomadic pastoralist to turn farmer and become static.

Some 10,000 years ago, as the last glaciation receded and the ice moved northwards off the face of Europe, the zones of climate travelled back with it. The tundra that grows up to the verges of the ice, the conifers that stand between it and the temperate zone, and the desert which lies between the temperate zone and the sub-tropical forest moved up behind. Early man was simultaneously reaching an apex of his pre-urban culture, quite by chance in one of the areas of the world in which nearly all the prototypes of our present crops existed together. Perhaps domestication of livestock had already begun; perhaps not. The nomad, whether hunter pure and simple or hunter-pastoralist, was faced with a deterioration in the means of his subsistence from decreasing rainfall and the desiccation of his land as the temperate zone moved northwards away from him. He had to move farther and farther afield in search of food, or decrease his numbers, or increase his resources. It was almost certainly in the triangle of country between the Mediterranean, the Persian Gulf and the Caspian Sea, and in a deteriorating climate which was turning a temperate region into dry steppe, that Mesolithic peoples began to sow what hitherto they had merely reaped. They took the seeds of the wild grasses which they had long been harvesting with their flint-edged sickles and deliberately planted them so that they should grow more plentifully and more conveniently. It is unlikely that there was one inventor of agriculture, one superior benefactor of all mankind. It must have been a commonplace of observation that grass seeds harvested but spilt were seen to have grown where they fell when a camp was reoccupied the following year. It was a natural step, needing a little imagination and some slight intelligence, to scatter some seed deliberately and wait around until the crop that grew from it was ready to be harvested. Both farming and a settled existence had begun; and the twilight fell on the day of the nomad.

Whether man had already tamed and turned to his domestic uses the wild creatures around him that were best fitted to the purpose, or whether that followed in the course of protecting his newly discovered crops from their ravages, is a question that will never be answered. The evidences appear together in the habitation sites: the marks of cereal cultivation coincide with the rise in the proportion of the bones of indubitably domesticated stock and the fall in the proportion of the animals of the chase. From these first beginnings, some time later than 10,000 B.C., agriculture and livestock husbandry spread from the points of origin as man moved north and west across the land released from the retreating ice-cover. He was driven out by the pressure of expanding population and the complex folk movements which took the Mediterranean builders of megaliths to the north-western extremities of Europe and the Goths from Sweden to the Black Sea.

The deliberate sowing of seed for growing a crop for food was the most important advance that mankind has ever made since it developed the powers of speech, conscious thought and fire-making. It had a deeper significance, a wider application, a more profound effect upon the future of humanity than the invention of the alphabet or the wheel. It made possible every later advance in civilization by relieving man from a daily, day-long preoccupation with food gathering and hunting.

The root crops and the brassicas—potatoes, turnips, cabbage, carrots—are newcomers upon the agricultural scene compared with the high antiquity of cereals—wheat, barley, oats and rye. No doubt edible roots were eaten by early man, as they still are by the Australian aborigine and other primitives; but no attempt appears to have been made to cultivate them deliberately, to select the most suitable, plant them, and harvest them. It was to the seeds of the wild grasses that the first agriculturists (to use that word exactly) looked. It is supposed that man harvested them with flint sickles, because what appear to be sickle teeth carry such lustre as the silicates in the ripe grasses impart. The earliest known cereals (which are, botanically, grasses) have been identified by the imprint which stray grains left in clay pots before firing and by the carbonized, burnt, grains which have been recovered, for example from Jarmo (7000 B.C.). None can point to a moment in time or a place upon the earth and say, here man first 'cultivated' a cereal. The border between the wild cereal and the domesticated cereal is uncertain, hazy and broad. It certainly happened that men (or women) selected from the wild grass seeds that they had been accustomed to collect and chew, or grind into flour, those which were the plumpest, most satisfying and the most pleasant to eat; and then planted them in the earth, so that they should grow to be harvested for the sowers' use. It would not have needed an unusually observant man to have noticed that where wild seeds had been dropped accidentally, there they grew profusely. It was a short step, but a pregnant one, to return a part of the harvested seed to the earth to grow again. It was such an observed miracle of re-birth that was at the heart of more than one early religion: even perhaps of Christianity, whose founder also 'rose again from the dead'.

How many varieties of grasses were chosen and then discarded, none can say: perhaps most varieties. Those that first survived the test of the long centuries and remain of supreme importance were wheat and barley. There have been many theories about the area of their original cultivation. The earlier ones, like those of the Russian Vavilov, were based upon the premise that the places of origin were likeliest to have been places where the largest number of wild varieties still exist; other theories are the product of the science of cytogenetics which now breeds the new varieties of cereals. All that it seems possible to say with certainty is that the progenitors of the barleys are wild plants of the Middle and Near East. The two-rowed barley (*Hordeum spontaneum*) found at Jarmo is still grown for grain and as a forage crop in the Middle East; the six-rowed barley, *H. agriocrithon*, also claimed as a wild original, seems to be a hybridization of a two-rowed wild barley and a domesticated six-rowed barley. The distinction between two and six rows in the ear is not merely a matter of botanical definition; it is of considerable practical importance because it governs both the quantity of the grain in the ear and the amount that remains to harvest without shedding.

The genetic constitution of wheat is more intricate. Botanists group wheats according to the number of chromosomes they contain (fourteen, twenty-eight or forty-two, hence diploid, tetraploid and hexaploid). Originally, there appear to have been a diploid type and a tetraploid type, of which the tetraploid was the ancestor of the Mediterranean macaroni wheats and the diploid a constituent of the later hexaploids among which are the modern bread wheats of northern Europe and America. The natural cross-breeding of these early wheats—again natives of the area between the Mediterranean and the Indian Ocean—laid down the bases of the arable husbandry of many thousands of years, man merely seizing upon the superior hybrids that arose naturally. It is only in recent decades that cereals have been constructively bred to a purpose, rather than accepted gratefully as an advance made by nature upon that which went before. Between them, nature and the pre-scientific farmer did wonderfully well.

Of the other cultivated crops, both rye and oats were probably weeds of wheat and barley. Both are hardier, more resistant to the colder climate of northern parts; and when they consistently stood and grew on unharmed after their host crops had failed they were eventually sown as cereals in their own right. Maize and sorghum are both exotics to Western Europe (as indeed are the other major cereal crops, for no wild progenitor of wheat or barley has been found there). Maize was certainly taken into cultivation from the wild state in Mexico some time before 4500 B.C. and reached Europe only recently; sorghum travelled north out of central Africa probably between 2000 and 1000 B.C.; and rice came from south-east Asia in about the same period. By the beginning of the Christian era, the principal components of crop husbandry were to man's hand, and many of them had been selected for so long for their usefulness that they were incomparably superior to the wild originals which had been first domesticated.

In order that plants might be 'cultivated', cultivation had to be invented. In natural conditions, the seed that falls ripe from the seed head is covered by decaying vegetation, or trodden into the earth by animals, or moved below the surface by the action of rain or frost. But this natural cultivation is wasteful of seed:

13

only a small proportion germinates, and of this, only a few plants survive to maturity. Such natural cultivation is, by human standards, grossly inefficient, giving the environment to succeed to only one seed in a dozen, a hundred, a thousand. To become effective, the arable husbandman had to do better than this; and since the soils suitable for growing plants were also those that already carried a natural cover of vegetation, some means had to be devised to place the seed at the right depth in the soil and free it from competition by other plants for air, light, water and plant food.

First, the soil had to be cleared of vegetable cover. In the areas of primary cultivation, where conditions were becoming arid, the easiest way to achieve this end was by felling and burning; and the flames which licked across the parched grass in high summer from camp fires would have set a patent example of this process of clearing. Or perhaps the vegetation was grazed bare. In either case, the surface of the soil was exposed to whatever primitive stirring tool was to hand. The digging stick and the acute-angled hoe were certainly among the first of these, the one imitating the action of the push hoe of today, the other the pull hoe. Both broke the surface of the earth, pulverized it to some extent in so doing, but did not invert a furrow slice, as does the modern plough. By about 3000 B.C. animal traction was being applied in both Meso-potamia and Egypt to the pull hoe by the simple expedient of extending the handle of the hoe into a shaft to which oxen could be yoked. From these primary focal points this invention, basic to the whole concept of civilization, spread with the migrating farmer to central Europe by 1500 B.C., and to northern Europe, the Low Countries and Britain by 1000 B.C.

Devices to prolong the short life of the wooden working parts quickly followed the coming of iron into common use. Of these the ploughshare was the principal—basically a pointed iron sock fixed over the point of the share beam which entered the un-broken soil first—with the plough sole following, to protect the base of the share beam as it slid along the bottom of the furrow. At a later date—sometime in the centuries immediately preceding the Christian era—the second fundamental parts of the plough were added: the coulter and breast which enabled a furrow slice to be cut at the base by the share and at the side by the coulter, and the slice pushed on to its side so that its burden of grass, weed or stubble could be partially covered and killed. All that now remained to make up the plough of modern times were the mouldboard to invert the furrow slice completely, thus offering a clean seedbed to the sower, and the wheeled carriage which stabilized the plough, reduced the friction, and eased the task of the plough animals in the yoke and the ploughman at the handle. Not, through fifty centuries, was there a competitor to this basic implement of cultivation devised perhaps by the banks of the Euphrates and the Tigris. Only in the last decade or two have been seen new concepts of earth-stirring, surface-loosening, and chemical non-cultivation coming into use. For five thousand years mankind has literally lived by the plough, and by the strength and skill and patience of the ploughman.

As a corollary to the development of an intensive agriculture serving a settled population, often grouped in large numbers in towns, a convenient form of carriage had to be devised for the harvested crop. Pack animals were one answer; but an incomplete one. Whether the wheeled cart was an agricultural invention or was one for military or social purposes is, naturally, unknown and unknowable. It had appeared in Mesopotamia before 3000 B.C., on the Asian steppes by 2500 B.C., and in central and northern Europe by about 1000 B.C. In its place of origin, almost certainly the Mesopotamian urban civilizations, it had solid wheels which rotated with the axle. This, in turn, seems not to have moved in the horizontal plane, which made the taking of a corner an awkward manoeuvre. The draught animals, most probably oxen, were yoked by the neck or horns to a central pole; and where four beasts were yoked abreast the outspanners pulled their neighbours' horns, there being no traces. The use of a cart presupposes open country, or at least reasonably negotiable tracks; although from the first many vehicles were designed to be dismountable so that the body could be detached and man-handled over difficult places.

A draught animal tugging a clumsy solid-wheeled cart along a rough Mesopotamian dirt track was, of course, a domesticated animal. It would be wrong to think of the domestication of farm livestock as a deliberate process begun by one man in one place at one time. It was almost certainly a matter of gradual association; or, as the late Professor F. E. Zeuner described it, the development of a symbiosis, the growth of a master and slave, or a host and parasite relationship, which when perfected has continued to exist until today. One cannot, of course, be didactic: the evidence is too slender, the processes too removed from our habits of thought, the time too distant ever to allow any firm statement as a fact of history. But symbiosis is so natural a development, and it is to be found so widely throughout wild life—from the hermit crab to the sheep tick—that man as an animal could scarcely have avoided it. The dog is perhaps the easiest, and certainly the earliest, example of human-nonhuman association. It was natural that the dog should form a loose, scavenging relationship with primitive, hunting man; as its kinsmen the jackal and the hyena scavenge in human communities today. But it was a hunting animal too, along with man; and early man may well have learnt to herd from the dog. It could have been only a short and rapid step to the domestication of the dog; probably by the rearing of orphaned puppies. It could also be maintained, in an Orwellian exaggeration that illuminates the obscurer truths, that the dog domesticated man. At the least, it was a symbiosis of equals: man permitting dog to scavenge, dog allowing man to utilize his powers of hunting and herding. Archaeology suggests that the dog was, in fact, man's first domestic animal: both the Natufian culture of pre-Neolithic Jericho (c. 9000 B.C.) and the rather later Mesolithic of northern Europe either had tame dogs or at least a growing association with half-wild dogs.

If the man-dog relationship was one between equals, man filled the role of parasite in the symbiotic association that grew between him and other animals. And, since symbiosis can only begin between creatures of similar habitat, man's arena of domestication was circumscribed by his mode of life. Man as nomad could convert to his continuing use other nomadic animals. Not until man became static could he develop a profitable and permanent symbiosis with other creatures whose habitat was restricted: the pig is the perfect example, as anyone will know who has tried to take a pig on a journey. Therefore man's earliest domesticated farm stock should be sought among his fellow nomads. The sheep came easily to hand; and literally so when man had taken dog into partnership. Indeed, man, sheep and dog may be said to have grown civilized together; man and dog in a symbiosis of equals, and man as a symbiotic parasite upon the domesticated sheep. The association was made the easier by the wide dispersal of wild sheep throughout prehistoric Europe and Asia; and by their gregariousness. The rounding up and control of a flock is more rewarding than the hunting and taming of an equal number of individuals. A battalion can be captured and imprisoned *en bloc*; to clear up several hundred snipers is tedious and time-consuming.

The association between man and cattle on a permanent basis probably had to await, or grew out of, a settled agriculture. Zeuner, indeed, in his philosophy of domestication held that wild cattle came to rob man's crops and stayed to be tamed; and not until civilized man needed power for traction in peace and for mobility in war did the horse come under control. As has so often been pointed out, it was accidents of circumstance and not a purposeful plan that led man to domesticate the few types that he did, out of the wide choice of species that lay to his hand. The domestic list is remarkably short: the goat and the sheep; reindeer, cattle, yaks, buffalo and two or three more similar; the pig, the elephant, camel, and the horse and its relatives; dogs, cats, rabbits; and some fowl. But in his apparently arbitrary choice for the provision of his meat and milk, his clothes, his transport, his tractive power and his servants, history has given proof of man's wisdom. It is hard to think of anything that could have served his various needs better than cow and sheep, horse and dog and camel.

The wisdom, of course, lay largely in man's ability to adapt the living material to his requirements. In their natural state, few of his victims—and that word is not wholly correct for in return for domesticity man has offered protection—few of his victims gave obvious promise of where their greatest usefulness would eventually lie: the sheep and its warm wool, the cow and its nutritious milk, the horse and its patient power, the dog and its unwavering obedience and response to training, are all associations deliberately bred by human masters into countless generations of malleable creatures.

Apart from the goat, the sheep was almost certainly the first of our farm livestock to be domesticated. Some would even say that its appearance within the fold of man's control preceded that of the dog. As yet, the earliest site at which it has been found in indisputably domestic contexts is at Zawi Chemi Shanidar, in northern Iraq, *c.* 9000 B.C. Its wide distribution in the wild state meant that it was to primitive man's hand when he did wish to adapt it to his purposes. Four types of wild sheep are commonly distinguished; but only two seem to have entered into the composition of our present breeds: the urial, now populating the belt of country from the Caucasus to the Punjab; and the moufflon, which until recently was to be found from Spain to Asia Minor. Both types were formerly much more widely dispersed.

One must here jettison the modern concept of the sheep as a thickly-woolled, white and submissive creature contentedly grazing the short pastures of the chalk downs of southern England and the sweet upland grasses of France and Switzerland. Sheep in the state of nature were usually heavily horned and wore a hairy coat predominantly reddish, with white and black admixture of colour, and ruffed around the neck. They grew only for winter warmth an undercoat of wool which rapidly moulted in spring. Their patent merit is their ability to turn rough herbage —from the gorse and heather of the Scottish hills to the scrub of arid Spanish plains—into meat and milk far more tolerantly than do cattle. It was this hairy, long-legged browser that the pastoralist took and, in a hundred centuries, bred into a specialized animal able to grow a score or a dozen pounds of the finest wool, able to reach a size at which it is worth killing for meat at three or four months—not singly but in litters of three or four nourished by the ewe's milk.

In some breeds of modern sheep relics of the primitive traits remain. The Soay, preserved in Whipsnade but also breeding prolifically on its island out in the Atlantic, still wears the heavy horns; and the archaic Loaghten of the hills of the Isle of Man may carry as many as six of them. The South Wales Mountain breed still boasts the ancient ruff: and the Welsh Mountain sheep of the less improved types has a pronounced hairiness of coat and a propensity to moult its fleece in patches from April onwards. The north German *Heidschnucke* has the reddish-brown coat, only slightly lightened by the grey underwool. The pure Merino of Spain and France, and its English kinsmen among the South Country horned breeds, all possess the ability to ovulate, conceive and bear young at all seasons of the year; in this they may perpetuate the traits and characters of a remote Mesopotamian ancestry, which moved slowly through Egypt and a score of centuries into north-west Africa and then across the Straits into Europe. The shreds of evidence, the hints, the faint resemblances, all make the tracing of the ancestry of the sheep a tantalizing, a frustrating, an absorbing exercise for the specialist. The layman is wise if he does not entangle himself in this thicket of history, darker and more tangled than any other in the history of the evolution of farming and its raw materials. He may be content if he does no more than note that in the earliest days of the domestication of the sheep, it was sought, tamed and bred first for its meat and milk, probably before it was noted that the woolly undercoat which it shed at the end of winter could be picked up, or plucked off, and spun and woven into an insulating, warm and rain-resistant fabric of surpassing worth to the weather-beaten and sun-baked nomad.

Where all is confusion in the genealogy of the sheep, the descent of cattle is comparative simplicity. If there had been no aurochs it would have been necessary to invent one: in other words, Western European breeds of cattle are sufficiently similar for a common ancestor to be postulated. There is, in fact, a wide measure of agreement that from the long-horned, tall, reddish-black *Bos primigenius* all the occidental cattle stock has descended. Its horn cores exist in large enough numbers in pre-Neolithic deposits and, progressively modified in size, turn up in excavations of Neolithic sites often enough to attest its wide dispersal in Europe and its gradual domestication, at some time later than that of the sheep, the goat and the dog. In its wild state, indeed, it survived as late as 1627, when the last known aurochs died in Poland; and it has since been reconstituted experimentally. It was in 1921 that the Hecks took a selection of certain European cattle—the Highland cattle from Scotland, the Swiss Brown and the Simmenthal from central Europe, Friesians from Holland and Corsican cattle—and in some years of interbreeding at the Munich Zoo achieved throwbacks to the aurochs type which, being bred on, threw offspring also true to aurochs type. After thirty years, there were forty apparently precise replicates of this European parent stock alive. The experiment was duplicated at the Berlin Zoo just before the Second World War, using British Park cattle and several south-west European breeds. Even more rapidly this time an aurochs was reconstituted, and these bore a close resemblance to cattle in the Spanish cave paintings. The Berlin aurochsen were lost during the war, but some stock from the Munich trial is in the zoological park there; and some that were set free in the forests of eastern Poland appear to have re-assumed the fierce temperaments of the wild species.

The aurochs in its original form persisted through early agricultural history, certainly to the days of the Roman Empire; and it may well be that the heavily horned breeds still to be found on the Atlantic fringes of Europe—notably the Highland and the Chillingham and other 'park cattle'—stand in direct and relatively unadulterated descent from this *Bos primigenius*. Its characteristic finching—the white streak that runs along the spine from neck to tail—that is so noticeable in the cave paintings at Lascaux, is also still to be found occasionally, notably in the last surviving handful of Gloucestershire cattle on some farms on the Badminton estate and rather more widely in some strains of Hereford cattle.

Alongside *Bos primigenius*, with its wide spread horns and large stature, a new type became increasingly common on Neolithic farm sites in Western Europe, the short-horned *Bos longifrons*— so called from its unusually long forehead above the orbits, heightened by a pronounced ridge between the horns. It appeared quite suddenly, and was probably an immigrant from Western Asia in one of the folk movements of the third millennium B.C. It survives in its purest form today in the Jersey, the closely similar Brown Swiss of the Alpine foothills, and, curiously, in the Shorthorn. All these come closer than do other European breeds to the popular image of the cow, patient, placid, docile and dewy-eyed, as different as may be from the dignified barbarity of the shaggy Highlander on his rainswept mountain and the muscular splendour of the white Charolais that grows at so prodigious a rate on its native French pastures. The popular image may catch the shadow of truth in this, in suspecting that *Bos primigenius* has, through several thousand years, tended to throw stock of beef type, and *Bos longifrons* the dairy cow. It is the sort of similarity which is detectable by the trained eye of the stockman, rather than by historical proof.

It is likely that the science of blood-grouping—which has already demonstrated the oriental affinities of the Jersey breed—may in time disentangle the skein of bovine descents. Neither this nor any other science is likely to elucidate the primary reasons for domesticating a creature apparently so intractable as *Bos primigenius* and its cousins; but the likelihood is that it was rendered tractable so that it might become tractive: for it was originally a beast of burden and of the yoke. Zeuner believed that the domestication of cattle was linked to the development of wheeled transport. Their value for meat, for milk, for the hide may have been secondary to this primary use; and the bullocks beside the shaft of the ox-cart trudging patiently along the Bavarian lanes between batteries of tourist cameras may perpetuate their first and ancient purpose.

A dichotomy more ancient than that which divides any other farm stock splits pig even today into two kinds: the house-pig and the forest-pig. In Europe the wild type, *Sus scrofa*, is the prototype of the grazing, browsing, digging pig. In eastern Asia *Sus vittatus*, banded, punched-in faced, is the father-type of the cottager's animal that lies and sleeps and fattens in its sty. Between west and east there has been a commingling of races beyond the wit of man to unravel. This simplification of type may seem too elementary, but it is fundamental to the history of pig. It was not until the British stockbreeder appreciated the distinction between the two in the eighteenth century (as the Neapolitan had two hundred years earlier) and imported the China pig, that the modern sophisticated baconer became a possibility. Domesticated pig dates from the early Neolithic:

Rütimeyer discovered it in his classic Swiss lake-dwelling excavations a century ago, and even then in his so-called turbary pig there was some trace of an Asiatic house-pig cross alongside the wild European type. But domestication as applied to pig may be an elastic term; and the forest ranched pig, only loosely and occasionally brought under human control, must have remained for far longer than any other farm animal scarcely within the fringes of domesticity.

The horse had no similar mundane agricultural beginning: it was too valuable in war, too great a symbol of status, often too sacred, to be harnessed to earthy purposes. Its relatives are numerous, its descent from a pigmy prototype well known. In the later prehistoric period it was, in Europe, a wild denizen of the wide plains; and it continued in its wild state into recent centuries in two main races—Przewalski's horse, still free in Mongolia and captive in some European zoos; and the Tarpan horse, which was reported to have become extinct in the Ukraine in 1851 and which, ever since, had periodically been reported as surviving, most latterly in the Urals in 1924. A school of thought, as old as Antonius, has held that the European heavy horse, exemplified in the English Shire and the Belgian Percheron, had a specific heavy horse ancestor. This school is now largely discredited, and the beginnings of the modern horse are sought in the Tarpan, a mousey-grey of about twelve hands with a black finching along the back as a continuation of the mane. It was probably domesticated in the steppes of southern Russia some time after 3000 B.C.; and once tamed, it turned the nomad into a warrior. It was in the natural state the least amenable of all later domesticated stock, except perhaps the camel; even now it still has to be broken, so that with each generation there has to be a new beginning in domestication. It was always so: Gruelin, who sought the wild Tarpan in Russia in 1769, recorded that 'they run with the utmost speed and at least twice as fast as a good tame horse'; and he reported that they preyed on the peasants' haystacks, two Tarpan devouring and spoiling one stack in a night, and they abducted and mated with the Russians' tame mares.

The early history of the domestic horse is as obscure as that of other stock. One of the earliest European sites at which horse bones have been found in sufficient quantity to suggest domestication is the Megalithic village at Dummer Lake in north-west Germany: but since wild horse was still being hunted in the Rhine valley in the eleventh century A.D., it is just as likely that the remains were of wild horses captured and slaughtered and then eaten. Probably the tame horse became common in central and western Europe only as late as 1000 B.C. and in Britain about 500 B.C., coming with the Bronze Age peoples who were equipped with wheeled vehicles.

Sheep and cattle, horse and pig are the stock of the husband-man, as popularly conceived. Other animals have played their parts in the farm scene, principal among them goat and fowl. The goat was perhaps among the earliest of all animals to be brought under human sway; but from its domestic beginnings with the Natufians of Palestine and in pre-pottery Jericho it has remained the poor man's milch beast, unlovely, unkempt, slightly comic, but immeasurably useful in places where neither the sheep, superior in meat and fleece quality, nor the cow, superior in milk yield, would thrive. It is adaptable to any vegetable diet, though naturally a browser of little regarded shrubs (and a great desiccator and desert-maker in arid lands in the process). Its earliest history, however, is bedevilled by the impossibility of distinguishing between its bones and those of its near kinsman the sheep in most prehistoric contexts. Analyses of animal remains in the archaeological reports time and again say no more than 'Goats (?) or sheep (?)'.

The domesticated fowl is the most exotic of our farm fauna, a native of the Indian forest, which has moved westwards with the centuries. The Persian conquests took it into Greece so that, said Aristophanes, even the poorest had his hen. Cheap and easy to rear and confine, it was a popular meat and a popular sacrifice. The Romans continued its westward migration, so that it is found on many Roman sites in Britain; but even before then the Celtic migrants of the early Iron Age had certainly at least introduced it into the island.

So man became possessed of the livestock and the plants and

the arts and tools of husbandry that permitted him to feed himself and his non-agricultural fellows more predictably, more liberally, more certainly than had his hunter-ancestors. But he did, consequentially, something else. From the very beginning farming altered the face of the earth; and as exploitation of the soil and its resources became ruthless, foolish and irresponsible it did even more than change the character of the cover of vegetation: it left the earth defenceless against excesses of weather that ruined large areas of the world. The extreme results of the invention of the plough and the release of domesticated stock from the natural control upon population growth lay, in prehistoric days, still far in the future. But grazing animal and cultivating man, separately or in combination, began immediately to impose upon nature a new pattern of plant growth. At first the digging stick in the hands of a primitive family would do no more than disturb, quite temporarily, the succession of plant growth; and when they passed on, the indigenous grasses resumed their occupation. Clearance of larger areas by burning left a more permanent mark. Intensive and close grazing by sheep so that the vegetation was bared to the earth and the browsing of cattle and goats which prevented natural regeneration of coppice—both in a climate moving from temperate to arid in the areas of the earliest farming—hastened the run-off of rain, accelerated evaporation, left the bare soil open to wind-blow. The result was a break in the chain of natural fertility, and a rapid desiccation; and as it occurred the family, their digging stick and their stock moved on to begin erosion elsewhere.

In the temperate zones to which farming progressed in the millennia before Christ, natural resistance to such exploitation was stronger: the rainfall was greater, the powers of regeneration more powerful, the soil more vigorous and fertile. The plough and the herd and flock did not desiccate and destroy; they merely tamed, very slowly, very painfully, and never completely, the natural cycle of vegetation. The soil became harnessed to man's use; but never irrevocably committed. In Mesopotamia, early cultivation, grazing and a declining rainfall have left whole countries in a condition in which, centuries or millennia after cultivation and intensive pastoralism have ceased, the desert then made still remains. In the Île de France, or the valleys of the Canton of Basel, or Shakespeare's Arden, the hand of man and mouth of animal need be removed only for a decade or a generation and first the weeds, and then the scrub, and finally thick woodland move in; and in a century the natural plant cover is in full occupation again.

CHAPTER TWO

First European Farmers

Compared with the lands in which farming originated, the countryside of Western Europe was of a nature to make its submission to man's early attempts at agricultural mastery brief and temporary. The challenge to the farmer differed both in degree and in kind from that which the Middle and Near East had offered to the first agriculturists. In Mesopotamia and India and Egypt the seed was nurtured in an earth that was becoming reluctant to grow anything at all. The first cultivators in Western Europe had to force a rampantly rich soil to turn its fertility to their crops and their needs and not squander it in the ancient thriftless ways, and to fight constantly against its return to wilderness. But even north of the Alps and west of the Rhine the challenge to man's strength and ingenuity was not everywhere the same; so the farmer and the pastoralist, as his craft spread westwards, fought the easier battles with nature first. He cultivated where there was least impediment to his plough; and stocked the most convenient and congenial pastures.

A few years ago one could confidently have said that these natural 'areas of primary settlement' were the chalk hills of southern England and of France, and the treeless slopes of the coasts of Lleyn or Morbihan: here the remains lie around in open abundance. It is now becoming evident that more is hidden than stands revealed. Careful aerial reconnaissance is discovering the signs of early farming and early habitation in places in England where none was suspected—deep in the Fens, in the valleys of Welland and Nene, and on many river gravels where the palimpsest of a score of centuries of later use had obliterated the readily visible marks of homes and cultivation. This drawing back of the curtain of time is proceeding fast in Britain; and beginning in Europe. Soon the whole prehistoric map may have to be redrawn.

Nonetheless, even though the full extent of early farming in Western Europe is still uncertain, the broad outline of its character is known. Both extent and character were governed then, as to a lesser degree they are now, by climate, elevation, soil type and communications; and as he moved westwards and northwards, agricultural man found these to be bewildering in their variety compared with the broad simplicities of the environment further east. The wide drying lands from Moab to the Euphrates, the endless hills from the Bosphorus to Harrapa, the vast monotonous plain of Russia had no counterpart in scale across the Danube and the Rhine. Here, by comparison, was an endless array of microclimates; and the character of the farming developed and pursued in them became infinitely diverse. Until the rise of mediaeval civilization and communication only such historical accidents as the Roman supremacy gave European agriculture a temporary semblance of coherence.

This diversity of microclimates imposed upon the earliest settler a diversity of farming patterns. How settlement proceeded can now only be guessed at. Rarely, if ever, could it have been an earlier parallel of the British colonization of North America, which transported seventeenth- and eighteenth-century farming practices across the Atlantic intact and entire. In some cases, certainly, folk movements may have carried the culture, with the people, *en masse*. In others, small parties—tribes or families—broke off from the circumference of civilization to pioneer. Most often the knowledge of agriculture and stock husbandry must have travelled alone, by word of mouth, by trader or fugitive. Through century after century, millennium after millennium, the process went on, leaving hints and shreds of evidence for the modern archaeological specialist to find, examine and interpret. Even slowly changing traditions in grain growing have been used to establish a nebulous but suggestive chain of folk movements in Western Europe in the last three thousand years of the pre-Christian period. But underlying the different patterns of culture, of custom and of habit there was a unifying force: broadly similar environments must, in farming, produce broadly similar answers, in due course. Here it is possible to grow a cereal, there only a goat can endure the hardship of a terrain, somewhere else

ingenious irrigation and a hot summer permit sub-tropical production in some favoured corner of a temperate zone, and ten
miles away there may be perpetual snow where nothing useful to
man survives. Very occasionally, one small people may exploit
this whole gamut of microclimates within their own tiny territory.
From very early days in the Val d'Anniviers running south from
the Rhône up the valley to the slopes of the Dent Blanche in the
Valais the remnants of an ancient eastern folk have done exactly
this, and have modified their old usage only with recent decades.
They migrated through the year from the Rhône, where they
sowed their cereals and grew their melons and apricots, up the
lateral valley into the heart of the Alps, making their hay, pastur-
ing their stock on the high mountain-sides in June and July, and
they returned below to harvest their crops in early autumn, leaving some of their animals to winter in the haybarns half-way
down. Where territories were wide and settlement thin, there
may well have been much of this migratory husbandry. It was
not the shifting, thriftless farming of the semi-nomad, but a skilful and economical use of a diversity of resources. Evidence for
such remains on Dartmoor from the whole prehistoric period; it
was practised in Wales long into historic times; and it was the
very foundation of the Spanish art of sheep husbandry and of
the fortunes made from Merino wool in the Estramadura. It is
important to remember this, that alongside the areas of stationary
farming there existed, from the earliest times to within a century
ago (and to within recent memory in the Valais) this mobile
husbandry, that gathered together into one economy many scattered resources from lowland arable to mountain pasture. Even
within such apparently homogeneous areas as the Chilterns and
the Wash, the shape of modern parish boundaries reveals traces
of mobility, with the mediaeval holding stretching from hillside
ploughland to riverside meadow and from dry winter grazing to
summer marshes.

Not only was the first European agriculture diverse, an occupation of many facets; it was also transitory, on the larger
historical time scale—and it has largely remained so, retaining a
pattern and a shape for a few generations, a few centuries, and
then changing within the framework laid down by the environ-

ment and the fluctuating climate. Southern Britain, where the prehistory of rural life has been reconstructed in more detail than in most other Western European regions, may serve as an example not only of the rapidly changing agricultural pattern but also of the complexity of cultural associations and folk movements. The earliest Neolithic farming people to arrive and settle in a land that had merely been hunted over for many thousands of years by Palaeolithic and Mesolithic man, brought with them their stock, a ready-made way of life, and the techniques of husbandry from the Mediterranean lands, by way of Switzerland and the Low Countries. They were in agricultural occupation in Europe, just across the English Channel, by 4000 B.C. The pressures behind them cannot have built up for some time, for it took them a thousand years to move across the few miles of sea to Britain. With unerring judgment, wrote the Danish botanist Helbaek, they then picked out for cultivation the moderately hilly country of calcareous soil north of Salisbury Plain, which was particularly suitable for their main bread corn, Emmer wheat, and for the small quantity of barley which they grew. They certainly chose these pervious chalk soils because they were dry to live on and easy to cultivate; not because they were forest free, for trees stretched through Britain, broken only by mountain and swamp and river, from sea to sea.

Their types of cereal are attested by the impressions of scattered grains baked into their pottery. Of their arable fields no trace remains, but the causewayed camps or cattle kraals—the earliest were Windmill Hill near Avebury and Robin Hood's Ball near Stonehenge—contained a wealth of bones of their oxen (the small, longhorned *B. primigenius*), their turbary sheep, the common European pig, and their dogs of large fox-terrier type; and also evidence of their cannibalism (perhaps ritual) and their liking for head hunting. Their domestic and agricultural traits appear suddenly in England, quite patently imported *en masse* some time soon after 3000 B.C. It was the island's first civilization: a culture that was mobile, for its stock must have been ferried across the English Channel; a culture that was organized and disciplined enough to construct large earthwork stockyards; a culture that grew flax for food and clothing; and a culture that was predominantly pastoral, with the fertility cults that go along with primitive livestock husbandry. It was a civilization that had gathered material and practices from both central Europe and the north European plain and brought them into a virgin and unsettled land, the first of a train of immigrants that was to continue to arrive in Britain from the Continent for the next four thousand years. It is only a slight exaggeration to say that Britain also at this time became an integral part of Europe, and it remained so until the end of the Middle Ages.

These primary Neolithic settlers in Southern Britain were in the next thousand years supplemented, modified and absorbed by other peoples of such diverse modes of life as the Northern Forest Cultures that moved up from Spain via the Rhineland. The gold —or the dross—that emerged from the amalgam was a warrior aristocracy that dominated Wessex at least and probably much of the country over the Channel. These were early heroes of Homeric cut, hard drinking (they grew, or had grown for them, mainly barley). They probably lived on the sweat of a dependent peasantry, who were descended in part from the ancient Mesolithic stock and were continuously fortified by land-hungry immigrants of less warlike a nature than their Late Neolithic and Early Bronze Age overlords, and they were supplied with bronze weapons by the travelling tinkers and with exotic jewellery by traders from the literate civilizations of the Mediterranean. The gloss of their barbaric civility was widely but thinly spread, establishing a tenuous unity between the Caspian Sea and North Africa, Poland and the British Isles. In this primitive commercial empire that was based on the Aegean there can be detected echoes of the legends of the Argonauts. The late J. F. S. Stone even suggested that, around 1500 B.C., the Mycenaeans may have had a trading post on the Wiltshire Avon. Romantically, this is a millennium that is a touchstone to the imagination. Agriculturally, it is a thin, nearly non-existent thousand years. In Wessex, as in Western Europe, the dominant culture may have been based upon a nomadism that paused, with its herds, long enough to sow and harvest a corn crop here and there. It could well have been a repetition of the earliest husbandry of the East as the pastoral peoples there learnt the arts of cultivation. This nomadic pattern was followed throughout Europe at this period; and it was almost certainly caused by the dry climatic period that stretched through the second millennium B.C., which made cereal growing difficult, if not impossible, on many of the thin, forest-free soils that had been cultivated in the earlier, wetter Neolithic Age. In a prairie climate men were driven to prairie ranching.

Away from the rich centres of the chalk downs which were being desiccated by the drying climate, there was some intensive settlement in areas which later became too wet for habitation. Dartmoor appears to have been thinly populated by pastoralists —and on its eastern slopes by some arable farmers—at periods during the Bronze Age. Their stonewalled enclosures contained upwards of sixty huts apiece. Some villages had nearly a hundred of these circular homes of thatch resting upon a low wall. The beginnings of an urge for privacy was perceptible in the bed-nook built into the wall like the bed-box of an old Welsh homestead. Stock pens, the interiors well trodden into mud, suggest the keeping of cattle rather than sheep. The arable settlements had fewer houses—only two to four—with half a dozen fields of half an acre each, walled in by slabs and boulders picked off the sur-face of the ground. At one place, at Gwithian in West Cornwall dated to 1400–1200 B.C., ploughmarks survive under blown sand. These 3–4in deep V-shaped furrows spaced 1–2ft apart cross where the field was ploughed both ways. In the headlands are the marks of the round-bladed spade, still in use in the area, where the land that the plough could not reach was dug by hand.

The change from this slightly modified pastoralism to some-thing that had, if not a modern, then at least a mediaeval look about it came quite quickly—again in the course of folk move-ments which imported ready-made farming practices. The days when Britain was to become an innovator, and not a follower, in agriculture still lay many, many centuries ahead. Somewhere around the twelfth century B.C. central and northern Europe entered upon a phase of turmoil—artistic, domestic and agricul-tural. This was itself a wave from disturbances in the civilizations of the Near East, and in the ripples that broke upon the shores of Britain both the Celtic people and the use of iron arrived. By

Celts there is implied no close racial relationship, merely the possession of a common source of language and a community of agricultural and other practices and customs, which had grown up among the tribes settled in the broad valley of the upper Danube in Austria and Bavaria, in the Swiss lake country, and later in the valley of the Rhine. Their end-products were the Celtic cultures of Dark Age Wales and Ireland.

Soon after 1000 B.C. the vanguard of this folk movement arrived in southern England, from northern France, bringing with them their characteristic rural economy. Half a millennium later the full flow of Celtic immigration began; and the descendants of their settlers formed the British nation for nearly a thousand years, until they were ousted by the Saxon. They were, in genotype, tall, fair, blue-eyed. They spoke a tongue that would today convey undertones of recognition to a Welshman. With their name of Pretani they moved over the borderline between prehistory and history. They were accustomed to live in rectangular houses that were the ancestors of the longhouses in which a small handful of their remote descendants still dwell in the Claerwen Valley and other remote pockets of the central Welsh massif. From now on, as one looks at the countryside through historical eyes, one everywhere still perceives such extant threads of an ancient, tangled and forgotten skein of rural economy—and of rural mentality as well, in the relics of Celtic religion and superstition, tradition and philosophy, from May Day to the mistletoe, from pseudo-druidism to the fear of deep woods.

The earliest farming manifestations in Britain of this new and distinctive culture were the enclosed holdings on the chalk hills of Sussex, with farmsteads, cattleways and small square fields. All these remain perceptible because when they went out of use cultivation also departed from these thin-soiled Downs. Here, and further west in Cranborne Chase, the land is still crisscrossed by boundary ditches, field banks and other earthworks that the archaeologist has patiently unravelled into arable fields, earth-walled stock roads and cattle kraals, superimposed one upon another as the agricultural pattern changed. In the rectangular houses the women spun and wove, ground the flour in querns, and doubtless entertained the itinerant bronzesmiths who

traded them the bracelets and other geegaws of the Late Bronze
Age. Their cereal cultivation is attested by the finds of carbonized
wheat and barley—occasionally a bushel or more that was over-
dried when it was parched in clay ovens (as at Statton in Suffolk)
for threshing, storage or grinding.

The fields are still marked by their square boundary banks,
and it has been inferred from their shape that a traction plough—
one drawn by animal power—had now arrived in Britain. Cross-
ploughing with a plough without a mouldboard is said to impose
a squareness on the field because only fields of roughly equal
width and length can conveniently be ploughed along and across;
a long narrow field gives the plough-team and plough length of
travel but an impossibly short width in which to cross-work. The
hoe has no mechanically imposed boundaries: one works as one
will, as anyone will realize who has seen a woman dig. This
theory of the association between plough type and field shape is
suspect, but the Celtic practice of cross-ploughing was dramatically demonstrated during the excavation of a pre-Roman Iron
Age hut at Alrum, Jutland, where, on cultivated ground that had
been covered by the hut floor, there were the marks of a plough
sole crossing at right-angles clearly to be seen. These Late Bronze
and Early Iron Age farmers also kept stock, as is attested by the
bones of cattle, sheep and pig; dog is still here; and a small horse
had entered into the rural economy. This was obviously the
beginning of a true mixed husbandry, of a pattern that was to be
unchanged basically until modern industrialization entered into
agriculture.

As the climate moved towards the peak of one of its long wet
periods and fresh waves of immigrants of Celts—now users of
iron—moved into Britain, the southern downlands must have
reached saturation point in population and cultivation as in soil
moisture. Given enough well-spaced rainfall, the Sussex Downs,
Salisbury Plain and the fingers of chalk upland that point out
from them are a primitive ploughman's paradise; easy of cultivation, although weed-infested; and free draining, although too
quickly leached of plant nutrients and always hungry for more.
It could have been now that cereal growing in southern Britain
reached a level, in extent and in techniques, that it was to maintain

until these arable lands were abandoned after the Romans left. What the modern farmer calls grain handling—the harvest and storage of cereals—reached a primitive perfection. Raised, rat-proof granaries have been postulated from the evidence of excavation; and deep, lined and lidded grain-storage pits were dug and periodically renewed. Farms, or complexes of farms that made up the typically Celtic holdings of the kin, became larger. One on Boscombe Down in Wiltshire, revealed during airfield levelling, covered seventy-six acres. It remained in occupation and use for at least 800 years, from the beginning of Iron Age A to the end of the Roman occupation. It survived the waves of Marnian and Belgic warrior-farmer immigrants to become, perhaps, a unit in the Roman Imperial Estate.

As has already been said, the types of arable crops grown are better documented than most other facets of prehistoric economy because it has been possible to identify them by their remains as impressions baked into pottery or by the grains themselves preserved in carbonized form.

It is unhelpful to the layman that the divisions of wheats, for example, made by the botanist and the archaeologist have little practical meaning for the farmer. The botanist groups wheats according to the number of chromosomes they contain, and the archaeologist into spelts, einkorn, Emmers and so on. The only common characteristic of the so-called spelts, which were the principal prehistoric wheats, is that all are difficult or impossible to thresh out easily unless they are heat-dried. The Large Spelt, which is the wheat species usually meant by the archaeologist when he speaks of spelt, requires in addition special treatment in milling. Despite this, it is still grown (by tradition and not for its utility) in parts of Germany, Spain and Switzerland, where a special machine—a *gerbegang*—is used to thresh it. It is this spelt which was the archaeologists' 'conspicuous cereal novelty' of the Iron Age sites in most of Western Europe, with a special concentration on the right bank of the middle Rhine (it is a coincidence that it is here that Large Spelt is still grown). Before this the archaeologists' 'Emmer' was the universal wheat type. It is probably the most primitive of the wheats, with the great demerit of shedding its grain too readily before harvest. To these, the Romans added club wheat (*Triticum compactum*), a short-eared and small-grained sort which yields a small crop. Where oats are found on pre-Roman sites in Britain they are all of the wild type (*Avena fatua*); rye was likewise a weed before the Romans introduced domestic sorts. The Celtic bean was known in Britain only in the lake villages of Glastonbury and Meare, where it had been brought by the remarkable bog-dwelling and prosperous craftsmen and farmers in their progress from southern Europe through Germany and France.

The phrase just used, 'likewise a weed', falls glibly from the superior height of twentieth-century taste. Early man despised nothing that came usefully to his sickle, as the carbonized cakes discovered at Glastonbury Lake village vividly show. These were analysed and were found to be made not only from the flour of wheat and barley but also that of the roughly ground seeds of wild oats, brome (*Bromus secalinus*) and orache (*Atriplex patula*). It is evident that the prehistoric grain crops were weedy, that the grain was ground unclean (it is difficult to suggest how the pre-historic farmer could have cleaned his threshed and winnowed cereal grains of the heavier and larger weed seeds), and that the quite strong flavours of some of these seeds were tolerated, perhaps even liked. The same indiscriminate acceptance of a broadly based flour is shown by the analysis of the contents of the stomachs of the Iron Age bodies preserved in the peat of the Danish bogs. Here again weed seeds were a common element in the diet, and in far greater variety than in the prehistoric cakes of Avalon. These Danes had eaten the seeds of various brassicas, fathen, knotweed, black bindweed, hempnettle and *Polygonum lapathifolium*. Stores of fathen and *P. lapathifolium* seeds pre-served in carbonized form in Iron Age houses in Jutland which had been burnt down suggest that even if these people were agriculturists in the strict meaning of the word, they did not despise the wild harvest. Perhaps some of these 'weeds' had been domesticated: for thousands of years the dividing line between wild and cultivated was very slight, in oats and polygonum as in pigs and horses.

While these Later Iron Age peoples were moving wave by

wave into Britain there were developing in the Mediterranean the civilization and the power of Rome. These in turn spread outwards over much of Europe.

In terms of rural history, the Roman occupation of Britain itself may be regarded as an alien chapter in a country story, rather like one of those sections of certain books that the reader is told he can skip without detriment to his understanding of the general theme. That is not true of some other parts of Western Europe, notably France, where the Roman contribution to the rural scene was absorbed and developed into an integral part of the agrarian whole. In Britain, when the Romans had left they might well never have been in the island for upwards of four hundred years—the period of time that separates us from the Armada or the boyhood of William Shakespeare. The Romans failed to signify because they came as aliens and remained aliens to the deepest, and agriculturally the effective, stratum in Britain —the peasant cultivator who was nearly the only man who was left to pass on the agrarian legacy of Rome after Roman Britain died.

Even in Gaul the Romanization of the country lessened as one passed northwards. The southern part of Gaul was virtually an extension of the highly commercialized north of Italy, its land owned by half-Italian magnates or even by rich senators of Rome itself, and its cities rivalling the capital in wealth. Northwards, where commerce dwindled and the towns were never more than tribal and market centres, the countryside was developed more by the Romanized tribal aristocracies than by Romans proper, and the real unit of civilization was not the town but the villa, the remains of which cover France in its thousands. When Rome had consolidated its position these provincial capitalists turned the valleys of the Rhine, the Moselle and the Meuse into a vast granary, wine-cellar and stockyard, with Treves and Cologne as the clearing houses. Across the Rhine began the land of isolated small farms, the land of the frontier posts, and the land of skirmishing with the unsubdued Celt.

Britain, after the Claudian invasion of A.D. 43, became an extension of this remoter Empire, a far-flung outpost of the rich agriculture of Rome's closer possessions. Its farming became intensive and commercialized only here and there. Britain remained for the great part a land of native farmers upon whom the civilities of Rome impinged rarely or not at all, and who carried their Celtic habits of life and agriculture through to the Dark Ages of the Saxon settlement. In Rostovtsev's vivid phrase, in the mass they remained, like the fellahin of Egypt, strangers to the very essence of Greco-Roman civilization.

The remains of the farms and settlements in Britain that can be dated to the Roman occupation lie thick upon the more easily cultivable parts, and aerial photography is now continually revealing new Roman farm sites. The Welland and Nene valleys of the East Midlands are filled with them, particularly on the borders of the Fens from John Clare's Helpston, past Lolham where he courted his Mary while 'little trotty wagtail waddled in the waterpudge' to Tallington; so are the Trent valley and the Ouse and Granta in Bedfordshire, Huntingdonshire and Cambridgeshire; and so the quiet Nor in Norfolk and the wide Severn. All these have been found to bear the marks of close settlement continuing through the Roman Occupation to the Saxon invasions. One would give much to see at first hand the contrast between the scarcely Romanized British peasant and Roman patrician: it cannot have been unlike that between the Indian villager and the family in the Viceregal Lodge. What was *not* different, or not very different, was the technique of food production. Scale certainly varied—the later Imperial estates in Britain were probably counted in tens of thousands of acres against the peasant's score or two. But in arable and livestock husbandry Rome added little to the methods of the Iron Age cultivator: immeasurably better road access, a new crop or two collected *en route* through Gaul and brought to Britain, more efficient bulk grain stores in the raised and ventilated stone-built granaries of the military settlements, and perhaps a heavier plough with a coulter, if the last Belgic wave of pre-Roman settlers had not already introduced it. For the rest, the peasant acquired the odd Samian pot from the mass-producing factories of Gaul and went on his own courses, doubtless paying his dues with grumbles and no gratitude for the Pax Romana. Perhaps the only real advance for which he could thank the Roman was the improvement in the technique of grinding his grain. Previously his flour had been produced laboriously between a stationary lower stone and an upper stone rubbed backwards and forwards over it. The more efficient rotary quern which replaced it was a primitive version of the upper and lower millstone of the later windmill and seems to have been copied from the portable mills used by the Roman army. The watermill itself was certainly a Roman introduction into Western Europe; it reached its acme in the mill at Barbegan, near Arles, where the output of flour from the sixteen millstones was sufficient to feed Rome itself.

In the popular mind the mark of the Roman in the country-side, not only in Britain but in all Western Europe, is the 'villa'. The villa was a rural homestead that varied in size and luxury from the enlarged farmhouse of the Belgic farmer at Lockleys near Welwyn, which expanded as Cobbett saw farmhouses blossom eighteen hundred years later with grand pianos and drawing-rooms, to the rural palace of Chedworth that was fit to be the Gloucestershire retreat of the imperial *legatus* or *procurator* himself. At both extremes, the villa was, in Collingwood's definition, 'an agricultural establishment'. In the more precise definition of the sixth-century *Digest*, the homestead and its buildings were the *villa*, the land the *ager*, and the complete estate the *fundus* or farm. In fact, at the upper limit the villa could have been no closer to a farmhouse than was Holkham Hall in Coke's heyday; it was smaller than that vast Palladian pile standing on rising ground just inland from Holkham marshes, but it was none the less comfortable, certainly better heated and equipped with baths, and it was serviced by a similar range of outbuildings from smithy to grain stores, and it was doubtless gardened and landscaped by an early Capability Brown, and buttressed by the industrial or political wealth of the Romano-Briton who owned it.

The villa had its vicissitudes—it is not necessary here to detail them—but through some centuries it dominated the British countryside south and east of the military zones of Wales and the North, as it stood subtly sited on its southern well-vista'd slope. In his villa the Romano-British gentleman farmer perhaps read the agricultural economies of the classical agronomists who gave birth to the science of farm management: pondered the costings by Cato and Verro of alternative farming systems, the anxieties of Columella over raising yields and lowering production expenses, the calculations of the Younger Pliny that if one extended one's area of cultivation one could reduce expenses by spreading the existing labour over more acres, and the details of the cereal-roots-cereal-forage rotation that anticipated the Norfolk Four-Course by nearly two thousand years (and had the additional advantage of doubling the output of work of the plough-team by winter- and spring-sown crops). Pondered, perhaps, but never did more—that we know of. In the end, the villa succumbed, less perhaps to barbarian attack than to the drying up of the markets for its produce during the disruption of the Empire.

The evidence is much too slender even to hint how far the man in the villa was a landlord of the peasant farms which often surrounded his *fundus*; and whether the peasant farm was an independent holding or a unit in a tribal community. There is a suggestion, however, that in some areas in Britain there was so much reclamation and peasant resettlement that these could have been elements in government planning. In the Fens—then passing through one of the phases of elevation, dryness and habitability—the purely peasant combination of simple dwellings and 'Celtic' fields, and the connection of the area by the Car Dyke canal and river with the military stations of the north, may point to the deliberate development of a newly won region for food production for the legions. Nucleated settlements around the Wash, in place of the traditional isolated farmstead, again suggest planned settlement. The same association of intensively sited small holdings and chain of communication could mean that Dorset was the granary for the Caerleon command in South Wales. If these explanations are true, neither project survived for long: the Fens were inundated in the third century A.D.; and the abandonment of the Wessex farmsteads and the appearance of stock enclosures suggest that the arable holdings were joined in one vast sheep run supplying wool to the imperial mills at Winchester.

It is certain that the Roman Province of Britain was not merely self-supporting; it was also able to export rural products, from grain to hides and woollens. This implies a wide exploitation of the land, for although there is scholarly dispute over the actual civil and military population of Britain during the Roman occupation, it is agreed that it was perhaps as high as half a million. Food production, therefore, ran at a high level; but it is likely that it came from the extent of the agriculture rather than from its intensity. It is not yet possible to say how much of England was farmed during the Roman Occupation. It is also surprising that so little is known about the techniques of farming in Roman Britain. There have been many ingenious theories built upon slender bases of fact, and much speculation masquerading as well-founded history. But despite the thoroughness of excavation and the mass of Roman agrarian literature (most based upon and written for Mediterranean climates and soils) it is impossible to say beyond reasonable doubt that the Romano-British husbandman tilled his ground thus; or bred his stock in that fashion; or even, with certainty, that the stock was so and so.

On the face of the land itself it is known that the Celtic square field continued in use and the Celtic farmer survived from the pre-Roman Iron Age to cultivate it. As Roman agriculture took the plough into areas of heavy loam never tilled before, it is reasonable to suppose that substantial and more effective ploughs were in use; and the discovery of heavy coulters and shares of various shapes supports the theory. But there is far too little evidence to substantiate the thesis that the Romano-Briton had a mouldboard plough with which the furrow slice could be turned over, or possessed a reversible plough with mouldboard and coulters turning the furrow to right or left. The scythe, appearing now for the first time, would certainly have made possible a more effective hay harvest for winter feed for the stock. Before the scythe evolved, and somewhat earlier the iron sickle, the harvesting of grass must have been a tedious and unrewarding job; and the rations of stock in winter may have been mainly the dry foliage of trees. One archaeologist, Sjobeck, has even calculated such a ration: the winter maintenance of a small beast of 6cwt would call for 1,000 leaf-sheaves of $4\frac{1}{2}$lb each. Both the longhorn and the shorthorn cattle (*B. primigenius* and *B. longifrons*) that the pre-Roman Iron Age husbandmen herded remained, together with the primitive Soay-like sheep. Remains of the grazing pig are numerous, but there is nearly no evidence of its complete domestication. The one certain livestock novelty is a larger horse, but it is not found in agricultural contexts, and it probably mounted the heavily-armed cataphracts who replaced the infantry legions. The quality of the cereals and pulses grown on Romano-British farms shows no advance on what had gone before, but rye was introduced and there were several additions to the vegetables grown. It is likely that the vegetable garden attached to the villa was, with the grapevine, among Rome's principal gifts to the economy of rural Britain.

Beyond this, it is unsafe to go. One could pile imagination upon flimsily buttressed assertions and top the lot with unsupported parallels with agricultural practices in the more Romanized provinces of Western Europe, or the Roman homeland itself; but there is a scarcity of hard facts that is remarkable from so long, so settled and so civilized a period in British history. Perhaps there are three reasons for the failure of Rome to make its mark on the farmland and practice of Britain as it did on those of Gaul. First, Britain was a barbarian land: the phrases were used of it 'on the edge of the habitable globe' and 'a country of the setting sun, remote from our world'. Secondly, Roman agricultural techniques were designed for dry-land farming and heat-loving crops; and Britain was wet and cold. And thirdly, Rome had many easier fields to plough: it was a reflection of the immensity of the Empire that when revolt destroyed the irrigation system in one North African province, 1,750,000 acres went out of cultivation. But it was probably the strangeness of the British environment that was the main factor in keeping agricultural practices on a leash. In the Mediterranean lands the farmer's main problem was the retention of moisture in the soil. To this end a two-course rotation was evolved in which a winter-sown cereal was followed by a full year's fallow so that two years' rain could be used to grow one crop, and cultivations were pursued interminably so that evaporation could be minimized. In Britain, the farmer's main problem is the disposal of surplus water in the soil; without drainage, the most fertile soils are useless. Again, in the Roman homeland, grazing was limited by summer drought so that much stock was stall-fed in summer, as in winter, with foliage, and with vetches, lucerne and other forage crops. Britain, on the contrary is, by its climate and soil types, a pastoral land.

Nearer home, the Roman was on more familiar soil. In Gaul itself the Rhône valley in the south and the wide fertile plains of the Marne further north were turned into granaries for the state buyers of corn—the *procuratores annonae*—who provisioned the legions in Germany and the civilians in Rome. Cologne had its barley market for the brewery trade. Even today, these areas have a marked advantage over the English arable counties in the ease in which they can bring their corn to harvest and store, from immense areas of easily tilled land, in weather which is perfect nine years out of ten. Rome was also able to introduce and develop in Gaul its own methods of wine-growing. From Bordeaux and elsewhere there grew up a large export trade of wine in amphorae—the great conical pottery jars—not least to Britain, where the domestic essays in viniculture can never have pleased any but the most thirsty and uncritical wine-bibber. Some effort was made to exploit the temperate grazing areas of Gaul, more akin to those of Italy than to those of Britain. In the central French uplands, now the home country of the white Charolais cattle, there was a considerable stock-rearing industry: indeed, it is probable that the Charolais itself, with its colour, its stature and its thigh developed nearly to the point of deformity, was brought from Italy where the Romanola cattle remain today in not dissimilar form. In the Roman Belgica, behind the Pas de Calais, the swine herded in the forest were slaughtered to produce salted hams for the tables of the Roman gourmets. Yet, across the English Channel, there is no evidence of significant development in livestock husbandry except for a suggestion that late in the occupation sheep flocks were increased to supply the export weavers. Perhaps the Wiltshire Horn sheep is a remote descendant of Roman stock imported for the purpose. Even the British villas, large though some of them were, were dwarfed by their Gaulish counterparts. The Charagan homestead near Toulouse was contained within a wall which enclosed forty acres of workers' houses and farm buildings; and the villa at Wilschbillig near Trier was surrounded by a wall fifty miles long.

Beside such magnificent spaciousness as this even the largest of the dwellings of the un-Romanized natives of the Western European provinces must have looked humble and primitive; but by any other standard they were often not insignificant and sometimes not uncomfortable. The high antiquity of the long-house has already been referred to. At the Neolithic village on the banks of the Federsee in Württemberg the rectangular dwellings which were its prototypes were up to a hundred feet long; were divided into two rooms, one of which contained hearth and oven; and were provided with floored forecourts. Even the famous house at Skara Brae in Orkney, with its stone bedsteads, wall-cupboards and cattle quarters, was better than a pre-war tenement room in the Gorbals of Glasgow, and probably smelt no more unsavoury. In the Neolithic period, longhouses of smaller size extended through Britain and over the Irish Sea to Ronaldsway in the Isle of Man and to Limerick. In northern Europe the longhouses even served communal purposes; what must have been a Neolithic tenement house at Barkaer in Djursland, Denmark, contained twenty-two compartments and was two hundred feet long and twenty feet wide. Longhouses in various forms persisted through the Bronze Age and into the Iron Age and historic times. Their purpose was always a dual one: to house both family and live and dead farming stock at either end. Usually the builders took the precaution of siting the byre on a lower level and to leeward of the dwelling. Of the numerous variations perhaps some Iron Age houses in Friesland (c. 100 B.C.) were the most extreme, with a central dwelling space and the aisles partitioned into cattle stalls.

The longhouse shape was a logical one, for the rectangular house is the easier to build, roof and enlarge by the addition of such aisles; and the span can be extended within the limits of the roof pitch by the insertion of aisle uprights without obstructing the central open space. And as for the proximity of the livestock, the stockman has always slept happily beside his animals, down to the modern groom in the stable and the herdsman in his cell in the stock-lines at the agricultural show.

Despite the age and the universality of the longhouse, the native dwelling in Britain had become, by the beginning of the Iron Age, usually circular in shape. There is no apparent good reason why this should have been so, apart from the ease with which the flimsier, temporary, tentlike structures could be dismantled and moved by a pastoral people. In the circular house, the roof rested either on the ground, like a wigwam, or on a low round wall of timber or stone, so that the shape resembled that of a high bell-tent. The size and character of these roundhouses ranged from the primitive small Bronze Age huts on Dartmoor, which may have been no more than summer booleys or shielings of a transhumant people, to the larger and more substantial circular Iron Age homesteads of Little Woodbury which were nearly fifty feet in diameter. In a roundhouse it was less easy to segregate stock and man, and only rarely—as at Ballacagan in the Isle of Man—does it seem to have served the dual purpose.

Throughout the occupation the current of barbarity, temporarily led into smooth channels by the civilization of Rome, flowed on in these primitive peasant houses; and when the power of Rome was removed it resumed its previous course. In much of Western Europe, the Roman methods of land use remained influential enough to survive in some degree. In Britain, Rome had scarcely scratched the surface of the lower rural stratum of life. When the highly organized villa agriculture ceased, partly because of Saxon destruction, partly because the international markets in which it sold its produce were closed to it, partly because of the disappearance of money from circulation, there seems to have been nothing left but the Iron Age Celt in his farmstead. To a divine observer, it was as if one had watched the film round for four hundred years; and this was where he came in.

CHAPTER THREE

The Mediaeval Scene

The legacy which Rome bequeathed to the inheritors of its power and its possessions in Western Europe varied greatly. In places, as in Britain, it was so small as to be scarcely perceptible today. In other regions little more than the faces of the men in the seats of power changed; and the thread of rural development was scarcely frayed, and never broken. None the less, by the attritions and the adjustments of time there was after the end of the Dark Ages little difference to be detected between the full inheritors and the dispossessed; for social and technical conditions had risen, or sunk, to a fairly common level. For this reason details of the continuity of Roman practices, habits and homes are of little importance to the general reader, though absorbing to the scholar of early mediaeval history, and they may be dismissed quite briefly here. What is important is the pattern of rural society which finally emerged.

Before the Roman Empire in the West collapsed from exterior barbarian pressure and interior economic decay, certain relationships between Rome and its neighbours had been allowed to develop. Roman farming at its height was a matter of individual enterprise, as far as we know at all levels. Communal agriculture as the Middle Ages knew it was unknown, certainly on the estate of the villa—the latifundia—and probably in the peasant farmstead, apart from such family co-operation as was natural and such tribal tribute as was extorted. There is no unequivocal evidence of the open field cultivations and the servile tenant labour on a great man's estate such as were the hallmarks of late mediaeval agrarian society in much—not all—of Western Europe. By its policy of enlightened racial tolerance, allied to the ruthless movement of whole peoples for military purposes, Rome before its collapse had allowed and encouraged to grow up the sort of free flow of 'nationalities' which has been repeated at

45

intervals ever since. As, today, London teems with Jamaicans, Bedford with Italians and Paris with North African colonials, so then there was hardly a Roman family without its Goth cook. German veterans of the legions settled everywhere, and Britons were resettled on the Rhine. The Empire was infiltrated, peacefully and purposefully, and when it was conquered the pattern of barbarian settlement was intensified, not introduced, and often the Roman himself was left in attenuated occupation.

Alongside this racial tolerance there had grown up a system of personal patronage in the later Empire. Under this many men, from military adventurers to the small peasants—the *clientela rusticorum*—had in the later years of the Roman Empire placed themselves under the protection of a local magnate and, ipso facto, placed their land in his power. This was far from being the mediaeval manor; but the system contained its germs within it. It spread widely, particularly when central authority began to decline rapidly; and in the heterogeneity of the Empire there were few areas in Western Europe where it was unknown.

The origins of what we have called patronage lie far back in history, probably remotely into prehistory, for it is difficult to conceive of a time when, several men being gathered together, one of them has not become the leader, the lord, of his companions; and as this leader grew in power other men put themselves under his protection with their families and their dependent kinsmen and their possessions. The seigneur guaranteed their safety and their livelihood; as Imperial Chemical Industries or Unilever today provide the livelihood and father the welfare of those who voluntarily join their organizations. A second source of the seigneurial network in Europe was the system of slave labour upon which the Roman estates had depended in early days. It was, however, wasteful in manpower and expensive in maintenance, as the owner of the villa came to realize. The herd of slaves was a form of capital which could be diminished by death or escape; it had to be fed, in sickness and in health, well enough to keep it alive to work and breed; but when it worked it did so badly, with an ill grace, and only under relentless supervision. Furthermore, as the Pax Romana became a universal reality and all and sundry could cry *Civis Romanus sum*, the convenient sources of supply of slave labour began to dry up. It was inevitable that the Roman estate owner should look elsewhere for better hands to work his lands. He was facing a situation such as was to overtake landed men periodically through history, of continuing to run his far-flung property with ease and profit when changes in economy and society were rendering the existing system unworkable: it occurred in these later days of the Roman Empire when slaves became difficult to obtain, control and operate; it occurred again several centuries later when Western Europe settled down into proto-nations under military domination; it occurred a third time during the economic and population crises of the fourteenth century. Each time there was a change in the contractual situation, the legal involvement, the degreee of dependence of the man who actually physically worked on the land.

The first change, and it was a gradual one, was the granting to slaves of their bodily freedom—their manumission—while their lord retained the right to their services as freed occupiers of a part of his estate. At the other end of the scale free men were coming in of their own volition to bind themselves for life to the lord. Through the centuries the balance between the wholly un-free and the nearly free moved this way and that. The freed slaves became hereditary tenants with considerable rights in custom, if not in law, as occurred in England when the last of the Saxon slaves disappeared from history after the Norman Conquest. On the other hand, free men owing only temporary allegiances got caught up in the feudal net, and the mediaeval courts were crowded with servile men who claimed the privileges of free birth.

The feudal system was based upon the principle of service, at first mainly military, later almost completely agricultural. Its origins lay in the dark centuries after Roman power in the West collapsed; its death came painfully and slowly, to France in the Revolution of 1789, to much of the rest of Europe in the middle of the nineteenth century, to England as recently as 1926 when the last empty relics of feudalism were swept away by the Law of Property Act. Its débris still lies abundantly around. At

Wallington, Bygrave and Clothall on the chalk Chilterns of Hertfordshire open fields and the rights that go with them still exist as relics of the system of manorial land divisions and tenures; throughout England lords of manors still claim empty privileges and sell their lordships expensively; jealously guarded sokes and liberties still fight the attempts of boundary commissions to rationalize local government; and societies battle for the preservation of manorial wastes.

These broad considerations of social structure in rural Europe have carried us a long way out of our period, when Rome was succumbing and the 'barbarians' were coming in. Beyond the borders of the Empire and infiltrating within it were barbari of Germanic race—the Ostrogoths and the Visigoths, the Vandals, the Burgundians and the Lombards. By the end of the fourth century A.D. they had spread from the plains of the Don and the hills of the Carpathians into Central Europe. Northwards other Germanic tribes—Angles, Saxons and Thuringians—were filling what is now (or was till 1946) modern Germany. To the civilized Roman they were barbaric because they had none of the attributes of his urban culture: they were politically disparate, mobile pastoralists, pagan, and uncommercial. In the two hundred years of the Great Invasions these barbarians overthrew the Roman social and economic structure of Western Europe and established in its place the eponymous societies of which many remain today still bearing the names of the founding peoples—England and Bavaria, Burgundy, Saxony and France itself. Then centuries of anarchy followed the centuries of invasion, when only occasional men of the calibre of Pepin and Charlemagne had the strength to impose their peace over wide territories and to control the advance of the Saracen in the south. But throughout these years of chaos two threads run, two strands of life which in time became firmly twisted into a rope which bound society together. One was the enduring need to farm, in order to eat, in order to live. The other was the military element which alone can establish a people in a new, hostile home. The barbarian was a warrior or a farmer, or often both in one person. The mediaeval society which grew slowly out of the Dark Ages was a combination of the two strands which took from the preceding civilization some elements of which we have already spoken: the system of patronage, the tenant bound to the soil, and the racial tolerance which, when the heat of conquest died down, allowed Saxon and Briton, Gaul and Frank to co-exist.

The pattern of society that emerged in Western Europe was intricate; but everywhere it was based upon the two simple elements of military man and peasant cultivator working together in the only environment they recognized or tolerated or desired, the countryside. The feudal system, the chain of custom and practice which bound the greatest lord to the lowest serf, came to flower at different times in different places, and in some areas it never took root at all. It was a Western European phenomenon found in its perfect form in that part of France which lies between the Loire and the Rhine. From this nucleus it radiated with decreasing importance into England, the Rhineland, southern France, Spain and Italy, but not to the seaboards of the Low Countries, or to Scandinavia, or to those parts of Britain that came under Danish influence. The constitution of the mediaeval manor in its classic form derived from the mutual dependence of lord and man. The seigneur, whether he was baron, minor local magnate or powerful ecclesiastical body, was nominal possessor of the manor under king or superior tenant-in-chief. Part of it, his demesne, was farmed for him by manorial officers; part was held in servile tenure by the peasant villeins; and part was held in unservile tenure by the free tenants. The servile tenants rendered agricultural and other services on the demesne, or elsewhere, together with payments in kind and cash, all as an early equivalent to rent. Free tenants were not liable to perform the servile forms of labour—ploughing, carrying and the like—that were the duty of the villeins; but over all men within his manor, free and servile, the seigneur exercised nearly complete legal powers, restrained only by the customs of the manor.

The chain of development of the classic manor from the patronage and the emancipation of slaves of late Roman days was forged gradually through the centuries. The first link was the symbiotic relationship between patron and patronized, between the big man who emancipated his slaves so that they might farm his estate more responsibly, profitably and effectively; and again between the big men and the undefended who came under his protection in times of trouble. This primary symbiosis was, socially and agriculturally, also the most enduring link. The links above it were interchangeable, often short-lived, frequently broken. The manors that grew out of the rural estates, large and small, acquired by inheritance or marriage or reclamation or conquest, were pawns in a national game of chess that went on endlessly for centuries: vast and scattered possessions building up in the hands of powerful men, becoming forfeit into royal hands, being redistributed among favourites and faithful followers as the reward and support of the military followers of king or baron and the source of supply of the unmounted men he took into battle. At the base of the pyramid were the dependent peasant farmers of the manor; at the top the knight who held the manor in fee, or, even more often as time went on, the ecclesiastical body to which the manor had been given so that the donor's soul might rest in paradise. At the height of its wealth the French abbey of St Germain-des-Prés held about 80,000 acres. Villein and lord were mutually dependent, and remained so until the King's peace was strong enough to guarantee the safety of the villein and until a cash economy had developed which enabled the lord to replace the villein labour on his land with hired men.

An example of the manor at the peak of its development may serve as a yardstick by which to measure the variations in the weight of the burdens which lay upon the shoulders of the peasant. Twenty-five miles north of London lies the town of Stevenage. The settlement began when, probably in the sixth century, some Saxon pioneer hewed out a farm for himself in the oak woods that grew in the heavy clay soil beside a Roman road. The lonely farm, or cluster of homesteads, grew into a sizeable village, and some time before King William's Domesday survey of 1086 it had come into the possession of the Abbey of Westminster, most probably by royal endowment. As a cleric, the Abbot himself may have been relieved of the duty to supply dependent knights to the royal muster; but around his manor lay other manors whose new owners were the knights and barons of William's army of adventurers, who had been rewarded with estates scattered throughout southern England: Bishop Robert of Bayeux, William's own brother; Peter de Valognes, sheriff of Hertfordshire; Robert Gernon, whose principal holdings lay in Essex. These great men took their knights and other followers to fight for William and his descendants—or against them. The Abbot had one more neighbour, a Saxon who managed to survive in possession of his patrimony—one Alvric Bush, whose few acres were later absorbed into the Abbey's manor. Today they lie submerged under the bricks and concrete of one of Stevenage New Town's 'neighbourhood areas'.

The manor of the Abbot and his monks grew into an efficiently run farm of classic manorial type; and two hundred years later, at the height of its development, the most intimate details of its administration, its crops and its tenants were written down in a fair and still legible Latin hand on a parchment roll which, dis-interred from the archives of the Public Record Office in London and dusted and unrolled, can be read with ease today. Fifteen servile tenants held virgates of twenty to thirty acres, for which they each paid 16d in cash a year, a bushel of wheat, two hens and fifteen eggs. Furthermore, each ploughed twelve acres of the Abbot's demesne land for him, and harrowed four acres; each performed three half-days' work a week on the demesne, and reaped half-an-acre at harvest; and at the peak period in autumn each was required to work on the demesne every half day in the week except Saturday and Sunday. Furthermore each of these larger tenants was obliged to cart produce from the demesne farm at Stevenage to the Abbey at Westminster twenty times in the year; the journey with the required loads of more than 2cwt of wheat or oats on the pack-horse must have taken the better part of two days. Below these small servile farmers of twenty or thirty acres there were sixteen minor tenants of a few acres each upon which were imposed somewhat less exacting rent in cash, kind and labour. In all cases the rent was attached to the holding, and not to the tenant; so the fact that nearly all the larger holdings became split by inheritance between a number of tenants meant that the duties also could be shared.

Standing apart from these servile tenants were the body of freeholders owing only a money rent to the manor; and although the number of servile tenancies remained nearly unchanged for some centuries after the Domesday Survey, the trickle of free-holders became a flood as new land was brought into cultivation from the Hertfordshire forest. Two hundred and fifty years after Domesday there were ninety-nine of them, against only thirty-one servile holdings; and the freeholders, besides being numerous, were also often substantial. One mediaeval opportunist gathered 949 acres into his hands, and his descendants were able to convert his possessions into a manor with many of the rights that were enjoyed by their great neighbour, the Abbot of Westminster himself: the right to hold courts and markets and pocket the proceeds thereof, the right to the heriot of the best beast on a tenant's death and a fine upon the marriage of a tenant's child, the right to grind all the corn of the tenants and subtract part in fee—and a long list of other rights and privileges that the servile tenants, bound to the soil, were unable to escape from one generation to another. To these unfree tenants the most burdensome obligation was the duty to work on the manorial demesne. Apart from the labour of a few landless men employed full-time on the Abbot's land all the tasks on the 539 acres of arable land were performed by the unfree tenantry, either on the enclosed fields of the demesne which amounted to 290 acres, or on the 249 acres which Westminster had which were mingled with the strips of the villagers on the common fields of the manor. After deductions of the grain, livestock and other produce used to feed the manorial staff and the tenants on the occasions when they were entitled to be provided with a meal during the day's work on the demesne—a matter nicely regulated by custom—the residue of the output of the Stevenage manor was carried to Westminster for the sustenance of the brethren.

The open fields to which reference has just been made were the second distinctive feature of the classic mediaeval manor. They were no more universal through Western Europe than was the 'manorial system' as it existed at Stevenage; but within the areas of ancient intensive cultivation it was the rule rather than the exception. Again, in the classic form, the arable land of the village was divided into two, three or more fields. In each of these every villager—be he lord of the manor, freeman or villein—held a number of nominally 'acre' strips, mingled with those of his fellows. In the simplest rotation of crops, one field was sown to cereals one year and the other left fallow, and vice versa the next year. In a three-course rotation one field was under autumn-sown wheat, one under spring-sown barley, and the third lay fallow so that it might be cleaned of weeds by summer ploughing and in order that its fertility might be allowed to build up again. Where two or more manors lay within one village, as they often—even usually—did, then the tenants of each manor shared the open fields in a system which is still far from clear. Very rapidly, on an historical time scale, the strips became so sub-divided that, where rationalization was not introduced to lay them conveniently together again by exchanges between holders, chaos in the end reigned. Again using Stevenage as an example, when the open fields were enclosed only a century ago the commissioners found that forty-eight freeholders and copyholders still held 760 acres of land in strips or with the ancient rights of common attached. The largest holding was that of the lord of the manor, the then reigning Lytton, who had $153\frac{1}{2}$ acres in fifty-six pieces descending in size from several acres down to $1\frac{1}{2}$ roods; among the glebe lands of Rector Blomfield were twenty-three acres in thirteen pieces lying in seven fields; and Martha Waby, a widow, had one acre composed of several strips, of which the smallest was eleven perches, the size of a garden allotment.

The centuries had, indeed, brought economic disaster to a system which had begun as a necessary essay in agricultural communism. In the beginning, open field farming can only have arisen because of the need to combine all the manpower, oxen and the tools of cultivation in clearing and ploughing the land of a pioneer settlement. The scene is not difficult to reconstruct: the small body of Saxon settlers laying aside their weapons at a likely spot, the felling of the trees and the long process of clearing the stumps, the joining of beasts in a communal plough-team, and the division of the ploughed land when the plough had passed on some basis of rough justice. As the crop was harvested all the land was thrown open so that the livestock could graze on the stubble and the weeds. After the second ploughing there was another redistribution of the land under cultivation. Very quickly this annual redistribution—if, indeed, that was the system—hardened into hereditary rights over a family entitlement, which became more and more scattered as new land was won and divided. And the rights of grazing over the stubbles and fallow, and over the communal pastures that were cleared, became consolidated into precise rights of user strictly regulated by custom. So tenacious of ancient usage is the countryman and so jealous is the landed man of his rights that some open arable fields and communal grazings still exist. The strip farming at Laxton in Nottinghamshire, the open field of Braunton behind the sand dunes of the North Devon coast, the hundreds of thousands of acres still lying under strip cultivation in France and Germany, the innumerable expanses of rough grass sterilized into parish commons and village greens, all these are the relics of a system that began thirteen, fourteen or fifteen centuries ago under the stress of conditions so hard, so hazardous and so bloody that the mind can now scarcely comprehend them.

It would be grievously wrong to leave the impression that this, and this only, was the pattern of early mediaeval farming. It was less than the half of it, and even that half rarely coincided exactly with the norms of manor and field system that have been cited. These norms were the average agricultural and social systems, as elusive as the average townsman of today, with his half a bowler hat, a tenth of an umbrella and one and five-eighths of a child: a convenient mean by which to assess the extent and nature of the aberrations therefrom. The main cause of the departure from the feudal system of manor, open field and servile tenants was probably the growth of a money economy. The nexus of manorial lord and manorial tenant evolved out of mutual instincts of self-preservation in a 'natural' economy—an economy, that is, in which if one did not grow one's own food one starved. The holder of an estate required his lands to be cultivated so that his large household should be fed. The peasant was a cultivator who, in unpeaceful times, desperately needed a lord for protection. Each party could meet the other's essential need; and without ample money in circulation and convenient markets for produce, neither could readily look to cash to seal the relationship. It was almost certainly because central Gaul—or France as it should now be called—suffered most from a collapsed economy and an absence of currency that it was here that manorialism took firmest root and first perfected itself. The eminent Dutch agricultural historian, Slicher van Bath, has argued this in his recent *Agrarian History of Western Europe*; and has likened the Carolingian Empire to an economic island denied all opportunity of foreign trade by its encirclement by Saracen, Magyar and Viking.

When William the Norman won England he transplanted this manorialism to his new possession, where it operated with steadily declining success for some centuries. But it failed to survive in, or perhaps never reached, the pastoral areas of Britain where cereal farming took second place to livestock rearing. By its nature, stock husbandry must primarily be production for market and not production for self-subsistence; and where commerce predominated there was no place for a system which was designed only to operate, and could only operate, where trade was impracticable. It was probably impossible for the intricate pattern of tenures on a manorial demesne to establish itself in such a society as, for instance, that of mediaeval Wales where transhumance dispatched the larger part of the scattered and isolated communities to the hills, with their stock, for months on end. For similar reasons, manorialism absented itself from the predominantly pastoral areas of north-western Europe—Ireland, Scotland, Scandinavia and the grazing lands of the continental shores of the North Sea. Nor did it establish itself in the areas of late reclamation, where land was brought into cultivation by pioneers who were rewarded with free tenancies by the nominal owners; or where land was reclaimed by large corporations—for example, the Cistercian abbeys—which proceeded to manage it without resort to the complex and agriculturally inefficient system of servile tenant labour. In a mediaeval world in which the restrictive covenants of custom hindered development on every hand, such unmanorialized areas and estates stood as islands of free enterprise in a sea of communal agriculture which worked to rules of a complexity and restrictiveness undreamed of by a modern trade unionist.

Dr. W. G. Hoskins, a muddy booted historian, has vividly reconstructed the mediaeval condition of the borderline county of

Devon, over much of which a fairly high rainfall and the impermeable Culm Measures make arable cropping a heartbreaking and unrewarding pursuit and a pastoral husbandry the only possible principal use of land. After the Saxon settlement this high, rolling upland was organized into large estates of up to 20,000 acres or more apiece; and if the Domesday survey correctly records the survival of earlier management patterns, these were worked mainly by slave labour. In the several hundred years between the settlement and 1086 these estates had been subdivided into parishes, further subdivided into manors, and upon each manor there had been constituted several isolated farmsteads. These appear to have been in the occupation of men who were nominally villeins; but they seem to have been involved hardly, if at all, in the normal week-works and boon works of the arable manors then actively evolving in the lowland zone, and even such involvement as there was must have rapidly disappeared, leaving in its place the modern system of cash rents and some of the legal accoutrements of feudalism. These farms then became just pastoral holdings in which the very minimum of cultivation was practised; or perhaps with none at all. The cereal needs of the peasant families were provided by cash purchases of grain, made with the proceeds of the sale of their stock—beef cattle, some wool, and the pigs from the extensive forest herds of pigs. The farmsteads which were formed often became mummified, as it were, so that it is still possible to identify the Domesday farms in many villages precisely, with their boundaries, nine hundred years old, still intact. And the groups of cottage holdings of the bordars and cottars around a little common pasture that has become a 'green' can still be recognized for what they were, perhaps even before King William and his adventurers came to England. These are the hamlets of the English West Country, that have stood with neither ambition nor expansion in a countryside where the serious, expansive farming is pursued on the large, isolated holdings which nestle in the hollows of the landscape. They, too, are often still little changed in name, extent or dwelling since mediaeval days.

There is, in Britain at least, a fairly clear-cut division in the degree of our knowledge of the husbandry that was practised before the Norman Conquest and that which followed it. The first is still dark; the other a long slow dawn leading over centuries into the full light of modern times. There was a continuity of method. As the Saxon introduced nothing in arable or live-stock husbandry that the Roman had not known, so the Norman in his turn contributed nothing except a new lord over the heads of the old peasantry. The pattern of Saxon farming can be guessed at, rather than proved. It was, above all else, a venture in pioneering. It is not yet possible to say exactly how far the Roman clearance of the forest cover had gone; but it is likely that much of the Midlands, some of East Anglia, and nearly all the North beyond the influence of York remained in the fifth century A.D. what they had been before the Romans came—under thick forest which was penetrated only by the military highways and a scattering of primitive pastoral settlements.

Then, in 1086, a recognizable England is seen to have taken shape. Nearly every city, town or village which exists now existed then in the pages of the Domesday Survey, sometimes in rudimentary form, sometimes as places of more substance than they are today; for time, while prospering some, has dealt unkindly with others. The total aspect of modern England in embryo had emerged by the time of Domesday, and this was the work of the Saxon peasantry over five largely unchronicled centuries: work in felling the forest, in burning, in ploughing by pioneers who practised the only culture and calling that they knew. There is no reason to suppose that the agriculture that they brought with them had advanced far beyond that which had been imported by their remote Iron Age predecessors seven or eight hundred years before; and no evidence that they borrowed anything from the ruins of the Romano-British husbandry which lay around them.

The help which even the science of place-names can give is slight: it reveals the obvious, that beans, wheat and barley, flax and clover were grown at Claverley, Linley, Whitcombe and Leasfurling; that cheese was made (at Keswick) and butter (at Butterley); that sheep and pigs were kept here, and that horses and cattle were bred there. It would be remarkable if such names and evidences had not survived, for what else could an agricultural and a pastoral people do but these very things? The early Saxon codes of laws hint at the communal husbandry that was certainly practised by necessity. In the century before the Norman Conquest, the first of a long chain of agrarian treatises gives firm evidence that the tenures and the peasant's work on the lord's demesne and the rents he paid in kind, that were the hallmarks of manorial organization, already existed in embryo, ready to be delivered by the Norman baronial midwife. About Saxon livestock, much nonsense has been written and believed. The theories of late Victorian historians of the importation by Saxons of red breeds of cattle, of the association between the Scandinavian marauders and settlers and the polled stock of eastern Britain, and of much else, have been elevated through the decades into facts. In truth, we know nearly nothing of pre-Norman livestock types.

There is more evidence for a widespread and extensive pig ranching than there is for other pastoral occupations. In 880 an earldorman died leaving to his family some woodland in Surrey and the 2,000 swine it contained. In the relatively rare literary sources of the times such references are frequent. They culminate in the records in the Exeter Domesday of herds of several thousand pigs in the woodlands of the Exe and Credy valleys. In Devon there were in all 264 swineherds paying rents for the grazing of nearly 1,500 pigs a year, and these were only a small part of the total herds. These herds probably roamed at will in most of the forests of the less thickly settled parts of the country, feeding upon the grass in the clearings, the beechmast, the acorns and the roots. The pigs of Spain which produce the gourmets' smoked raw lean pigmeat, like smoked salmon, do the same to this day, as did the herds of northern Gaul for the Roman epicure. Any woodland, indeed, throughout England was assessed in value on its actual or potential population of pigs. That these were long-bristled, razor-backed and slow-maturing is not in doubt, for there was no marked improvement in pig type until the seventeenth century; and a large part of the mediaeval woodland pig herds must have scarcely crossed the borderland of domesticity and have gone wild as readily as a country cat will become feral today.

If these half-wild swine are far from the modern conception of a pig as an indolent animal penned throughout its short life, so is the mediaeval beast far from the image of the twentieth-century dairy cow, placidly yielding its thousand gallons of milk a year. And discussion of the cattle of Britain in Saxon times must proceed warily because of the common subconscious association between the ox and the plough-team. In fact, positive proof of a wide use of beasts in the yoke is lacking, although such use is likely. In spite of their value for riding and as a symbol of social position, the descendants of the Roman horse and the large native population of ponies may have been used as traction animals on the land. References to stud farms suggest that they were bred in some numbers, and the Domesday surveys record numbers of wild and unbroken mares, particularly in woodland manors: the Exmoor settlement of Brendon possessed 104. None-the-less the popular picture of the ox as the agricultural maid-of-all-work of the time may not be far wrong. It had many advantages over the horse: it lived on rougher fare than the horse, which at work required a ration of oats; it needed little breaking; it pulled more steadily in the yoke and was far more easily harnessed; and when it was past work it provided welcome, though tough, meat for the table.

The cow was probably little regarded as a milch beast, for it may have given scarcely more milk than that needed to rear its calf. The role of dairy animal was reserved for the sheep. If proof is needed of this, one need only turn to some of the many references in Saxon charters to rents of sheep farms paid in cheese. This association between the ewe and the cheese vat is very ancient; it survived into the 1950s in Wales and flourishes still in France. The milk yield of a ewe bred for its dairy qualities can be high; in the Near East it sometimes exceeds two hundred gallons in a lactation, and as near to Britain as the German-Dutch border the East Friesland and Westphalian breeds still milk heavily. It is probable that before the rise of the wool trade in England in later mediaeval times and the consequent breeding of sheep for fleece weight and quality rather than for prolificacy and milkiness, the England breeds of sheep were equally heavy milkers. The technique of ewe milking differs from that of cow milking in that the ewe is milked from the rear and not the side, and the small hands of a woman are really necessary for the task. Different tethering methods are also needed, a common one being the ewe ladder. I saw one of these in use on a Brecon farm as recently as 1954. It was no more than an ordinary ladder placed horizontally, and the ewe's head was secured between a pair of rungs. Such a device is likely to have a long history of use behind it, and may well have been the method with which the Saxon shepherd-dairymaid held her ewe flock in the field. Such a practice would be comical today, so far has the sheep retreated again from domesticity.

The eleventh-century sheep population of Britain was certainly very large. In those counties where stock numbers were entered in the Domesday Survey those of the sheep exceed those of all other stock: in Norfolk there were twenty sheep for every head of cattle and for every three pigs on the demesnes of the lords of the manor, and it is likely that peasant flocks would be proportionately even larger. Often perhaps, like the herds of pigs in the West Country, many Saxon flocks of sheep grazed over wide areas of waste—on the thin pastures of the Breckland sands, for instance, or the maritime marshes, ignoring such private rights as existed. Similarly the vast mobile flocks of mediaeval Spain and Italy grazed where they chose as they passed like locusts over the countryside between lowland and mountain pasture. In England, however, where rights of every sort became closely and jealously hedged about by law and custom, the common sheep grazings soon came to be regulated with some precision: the Essex islands of Foulness, Canvey and Wallasey, for instance, were sheeped hoof-under-hoof, as the phrase went, with flocks of stipulated size from certain inland manors. It has been calculated that in 1086 there were at least 92,000 sheep in Essex; and in 1937 there were only 78,000.

The convenience and the value of sheep in a rural society that was still pioneering a relatively uncultivated country were considerable. Compared with both ox and pig this was an animal that could be controlled with ease; was undemanding in its needs; provided three of the commodities that were of supreme importance in a peasant life—milk, wool and fertility; and was cheap enough to form part of the chattels of even the humblest husbandman. Its only competitor in the economy of the early mediaeval cottager was its cousin the goat. And not only of the cottager, for on the wide stock ranches on the Somerset Mendips that belonged to the greatest men in the realm large numbers of goats ran with the flocks of milch sheep. The royal manor of Chewton Mendip had fifty she-goats with the eight hundred ewes in its cheese-making 'bercary'; and the Abbot of Glastonbury had forty-two goats with his five hundred sheep. After this period the population of goats in Britain declined steadily; rarely are they mentioned later; and the sole survivors of the mediaeval stock are probably the elusive wild goats of Snowdon and other mountains of Britain.

Much of this widespread Saxon and early Norman stock husbandry stood outside the manorial framework of servile peasant and open field. It made use of the wide stretches of countryside that had not yet succumbed, and would never succumb, to the plough—the high, thin soils of Mendip scarred by Roman lead-working; the maritime marshes of East Anglia, now the lonely retreats of bird-watchers and duck-shooters; the wind-mishapen forest hills of Exmoor and Brendon that revert so quickly to their natural cover once the temporary hand of man is removed; and the dense, primeval woodland of which scraps survive as nature reserves or fox coverts. Such extra-manorial livestock farming dwindled in extent as ploughable Britain was reclaimed and as the new Norman lords imposed, or accelerated the Saxon development of, manorialization on the classic model that they had learnt in Western Europe.

In Britain, farming had to arise anew from the ashes of the Roman countryside. In Europe there had been some degree of continuity. In France in particular the organization and the methods of agriculture continued to grow steadily after the power of Rome, but not its traditions of husbandry, had gone. There may, indeed, have been a few exceptions to the general rule that in the fifth century England relapsed, agriculturally as well as socially and economically, into a barbarity out of which it took the land and the Saxon pioneers several centuries to climb again. But if there were such exceptions, they were rare and they are now unidentifiable: a continuity of squatters in the corner of a crumbling town or of a country estate fast reverting to wilderness. Time could prove this view wrong. Professor H. P. R. Finberg has, indeed, suggested that there may be a thin chain of continuity between Celtic farming and the present day in the holding called Treable, on the northern edge of Dartmoor. But for all practical purposes, the Saxon in England had to begin all over again; while his continental contemporary stepped, perhaps often a little clumsily, into the agrarian shoes of his skilful predecessor in occupation.

Thus it was that throughout most of the Middle Ages the agricultural techniques on the West European mainland remained significantly in advance of those in England.

CHAPTER FOUR

Monetary Economy

The words 'subsistence agriculture' have a primitive ring about them, a connotation of backwardness and poverty, a flavour of defeatism and lack of initiative. In a society in which trade is absent there is no need for more than the growing of such food as will be required by the husbandman, his family and his masters. At no time, perhaps, since the very earliest days has some form of tribute not been required from the peasant, in rent or taxes in kind. But, that commitment being met, there remain only the needs of the household to be satisfied. In the economy of Saxon Britain there was rarely the opportunity, or the compulsion, for anything more; there is little evidence for the existence of markets at which surplus could be bartered; so that the family—or, at most, the village—was a self-sufficient entity, neither needing anything from outside nor looking for external aid. Such a state of completeness has always had a fascination for many people who have never been under the necessity to suffer it; and from the mediaeval monastic withdrawals from the material and mental world through to the modern experiments by desert islanders there have been constant attempts to recapture its pristine and simple satisfactions. The history of agricultural progress, however, has been the history of men's successful efforts to break out of the constrictive bands, both physical and spiritual, of self-subsistence into the free world of commerce. In particular, the mediaeval agriculturist made his greatest strides in techniques under the stresses and challenges of a monetary economy; and in the process changed rural Britain from a narrow world of sweat and toil into a place with the leisure, the money and the desire for the better things of life—domestic comfort, the pleasure of good building, and the arts.

As has been said, some rural societies in Western Europe moved towards these ends while Britain still struggled to re-establish itself. In the Mediterranean area the methods of Roman husbandry continued with little interruption north of the area of Saracen influence. In early Capetan France periods of feudal anarchy hindered the smooth growth of agriculture, particularly in those villages which did not lie under the immediate protection of a seigneur of some power, but even here desolation was soon remedied. The development of French towns in particular bestowed a security and a ready market at one and the same time on the peasant farmers of the locality, not a few of whom were themselves townsmen practising their calling in the town fields: it was recorded of Cologne in the eleventh century that the city was empty at harvest time. Beyond the borders of surviving intensive Roman development, the tenth and eleventh and twelfth centuries witness a phase of unprecedented agricultural expansion by forest clearance, undertaken largely by men who had been deliberately settled for that purpose—the so-called hospites. In this the monastic order of Cîteaux was a dominant force. It was founded so that the brethren might pursue the things of the spirit in solitary places, where they were to maintain themselves by the sweat of their brows. They were so vastly successful in taming the wilderness of the forests and the hills in the process, adding reclaimed land to their original holdings and managing the whole with superb efficiency, that the mediaeval Welsh historian Giraldus Cambrensis wrote of them that by piety they had become so rich that they stood in danger of the sin of avarice as they spread their prayers and their ploughs to the uttermost parts of Western Europe, from the coast of Welsh Cardiganshire to the Slavonic lands of Germany. The forest was limitless, but they and the hospites of lay lords bit their way into it as they did in northern and eastern France, while the Low Countries were being developed in the form of polders—a process only now being completed as the last of the Zuider Zee becomes solid, fertile farmland. The work began under Count Baldwin V, in the mid-eleventh century—a man who 'made much unprofitable land fruitful' by drainage into dykes and canals.

In the winning and improvement of this great area of new farmland, techniques—particularly in arable husbandry—were borrowed and adapted from the regions of old civilization so that gradually a peasant and seigneurial agriculture which had advanced little in north west Europe from its pre-Roman Celtic condition became a source of technical inspiration for the inheritors of the newly pioneered land of Britain. Perhaps the most important of the advances—and virtually the only one open to arable farmers before science and technology made it possible to produce better seeds, fertilizers and implements—was the development of more sophisticated rotations. There is little doubt that at the very beginning of cereal husbandry an area of land was cleared, cultivated and then cropped year after year until it became exhausted. The next step forward, made necessary when land became relatively scarce, was to take a crop one year and allow the field to lie fallow and regenerate the next: this was essentially the husbandry of classical Rome, where the moisture content of the soil had to be allowed to build up in areas of low rainfall. But this most elementary of two-course rotations—crop, fallow, crop, fallow *ad infinitum*—was too wasteful to continue in regions where enough rain fell through the year to sustain an annual crop. In particular, it made only half use of the land; and it concentrated all the work of cultivation and sowing into a short space of time, either autumn or spring according to whether the cereal crop stood through the winter or not. The Roman agronomists had, as we have seen, been aware of this; and at least theorized about it. It was the ninth- and tenth-century farmers of the territory north of the intensively cultivated Roman areas —notably Alsace and Burgundy—who left the first documented evidence of the use of a three-course rotation. In Carolingian Gaul this was widely applied on the progressive royal and monastic estates, so that two-thirds of the land was in productive use each year and only one-third lay uncropped; and the plough-teams and the broadcasters of the seed were employed in cultivating and sowing over a period twice as long as was possible with a two-course rotation. They were thus enabled to till upwards of twice as much land with the same resources of men, traction animals and implements. The three-course rotation had one disadvantage, that it reduced the area of fallow grazing available to the livestock from half the tillage area to one-third. How inconvenient this was varied with the number of stock to be grazed and the area of permanent pasture and ley meadow available; but all the evidence points to a shortage of keep that was often desperate, suggesting that the smaller peasants whose animals existed largely on the weed growth of the fallow and stubbles were hard hit when an improving seigneur or consortium of larger peasants moved to three courses. This advance was, of course, not always possible, even though it was desired; for manure was scarce, and on the lighter soils—the chalks especially —natural fertility was too low to permit the husbandman to follow the lead of his neighbours on stronger, heavy land with greater reserves of plant nutrients.

This was probably the most important advance in arable farming in mediaeval times, this increase in the use of available resources in land and labour. Some artificial aids to larger yields were also developed, again mainly in central France. More intensive cropping took a heavy toll of soil nutrients and weakened the soil structure by depleting the humus which kept it friable and retentive of moisture in drought. One of the innovations was the practice later called denshiring in England because it was believed to have originated in Devonshire; by it the turf was stripped, was allowed to dry and was then burnt in large, slow-smouldering heaps. The residue of ash was rich in potash, and the fire consumed such harmful pests as inhabited the top few inches of soil —notably the wireworms—so that a few heavy crops were then taken before the loss of organic matter in the fire made itself felt. Such paring and burning was practised in sixth-century Spain, whence it spread to the arable lands of Carolingian France. It is possible that a second of the early mediaeval methods of soil amelioration began in Roman Britain—Pliny said that it did. This was marling, strictly the excavation and spreading of a workable calcareous clay loam over a thin topsoil to give it body, or more generally the application of a thin soil to a thick one or vice versa. The practice was almost certainly abandoned in Britain after the end of the Roman occupation, but it was being encouraged in France in the ninth century and during the next few centuries it had become common in the northern arable areas between the Île de France and the English Channel. There, as in England, it left two marks: a semi-permanent one of heavier crops, which persisted for some decades after the application of marl; and the permanent one of marl pits which indent many fields to this day, and by short-memoried people are now identified as the result of bomb or landmine. One other method of increasing the fertility of the soil was developed within the system of manorial tenures which evolved in France; the *jus faldae* or the right of the seigneur to have the livestock of the manor folded over selected areas of his demesne to act as walking dungcarts. Its modern descendant, still practised particularly on the thinner chalk soils, is the hurdling of sheep on a winter feed crop of turnips or rape so that the land may be enriched by the droppings and consolidated by the feet of the sheep for the following cereal crop. Such land is still known to the older generation as 'sheep and barley farms', though the flock may not have been folded over it for several decades.

That yields on dry soils could be greatly increased by irrigation was a discovery that was certainly made in dynastic Egypt, if not in even earlier times farther east; and it was widely adopted by the sophisticated Roman landowner, particularly in the north African territories. It is probable that it was there assumed by the Arab conquerors and taken over the Mediterranean into southern Spain, along with such semi-tropical crops as cotton, sugar-cane and rice. The Arab irrigation system was a complex and effective network of channels fed by a lifting device, powered by hand or animal; and it was copied in southern France at a fairly early date, whence it spread into the upper valley of the Rhône and later into south-western Germany. The more northerly manifestation, or adaptation, of this ancient practice was the technique of water-meadowing, in which shallow channels were led from a watercourse and along these the meadow was flooded to a depth controlled by sluice gates. This performed two tasks: it covered the grass sward with a thin layer of fertile river silt; and it raised the water table to allow the grass to make exceptionally good growth, however short the rainfall of spring and summer might be. Irrigation of this sort was more primitive than the technically advanced system of the Arabian farmers, and it was confined to low-lying river fields and maritime marshes where floodwater rose naturally to ground level when the watercourse was in spate. Nonetheless, it was useful enough to be borrowed by English landlords, particularly in the valleys of Wiltshire, where it lingers in use to this day. The skill of the early drainage engineers of the Low Countries also owes something to this Saracen inspiration; and it was from them that the monastic improvers of the extensive English marshes of Romney and the Glastonbury estates learnt the techniques of adjusting the water tables of these dyke-drained areas to keep grass growing strongly. Soil water was the one element which mediaeval man discovered how to control with some success in areas where unified and enlightened ownership made an extensive drainage scheme possible. Elsewhere, field drainage was an art and a science that remained unmastered; and in heavy and retentive soils excessive water continued to keep the ground sodden and sour to the serious detriment, or sometimes total loss, of crops.

Such surface drainage as was achieved on arable land was the work of the improved ploughs, because the method in which these were used formed a furrow between each bout to act as a miniature dyke along which surface water could run away—or at least accumulate. There are three main types of plough used for breaking the ground. The Mediterranean *araire*, inherited from the Near East, merely had a share which ran through the soil and disturbed it enough to make a seedbed and destroy the shallower rooting weeds. It imitated the action of the snout of the rootling pig, and was essentially a dry-land implement which exposed as little broken ground as possible to the drying action of the sun; but it was cheap and easy to construct so it came into use, and was long used, by poorer peasant cultivators everywhere. Secondly, there was the fixed mouldboard plough which cut and turned over to the right side a furrow slice that was several inches deep. And third, there was the plough with the reversible mouldboard which could be adjusted to turn the furrow slice to right or to left. With this reversible—or, as it is illogically called, one-way—plough, the ploughman could go up and down the field turning furrow against furrow by reversing the mouldboard at the end of each bout. All the furrow slices then lay in one direction (to the right of the first furrow) and the field could be cultivated down with harrows to a level surface. The fixed mouldboard plough, however, by moving the cut slice only to the right, imposed a different surface pattern: the ploughman ploughed an opening rig of two furrows laid against each other (and usually then split apart again to break up the unploughed ground below them), and continued to plough round and round this centre-point until he reached the stage when the distance he travelled with his plough out of the ground at each end of the bout became excessive. He thereupon started and completed another bout alongside. Between each pair of bouts lay a miniature ditch formed by two furrow slices being turned outwards from it, one to the first bout on the one side and the other to the second bout alongside it. The height of the ridge along the opening rig and the depth of the declivity along the closing furrows became accentuated. When the bout coincided, as it seems often to have done, with one strip in the mediaeval open field, and the opening and closing furrows had always to be made in the same places, there was no opportunity to restore a level surface by ploughing ridge back into furrow periodically. It was one or both of these reasons that built up the pattern of ridge-and-furrow that lies beneath the permanent grass sward in many fields of English Midland counties today. And it was this characteristic mode of work of the fixed mouldboard plough that formed the drainage furrows between the ridges in fields on heavy soils that would otherwise have lain uniformly sodden in areas of heavier rainfall than that of the relatively arid Mediterranean lands.

It was likely that the fixed mouldboard plough was developed —probably in the Allemanic region of the Carolingian Empire (approximately the modern Bavaria)—from a Romano-Germanic prototype of a wheeled implement with share and coulter but no mouldboard. It was primarily a plough which broke the surface of heavy soils to a degree and to a depth that covered and killed the thick top growth of weeds that luxuriated in a wet fertility that was unknown in dry and dusty Italy. It also loosened and aerated the soil as the hoe-like *araire* never could, and it allowed wind and sun and frost to penetrate to break up the glutinous clods into a fine seedbed in which cereal seeds could germinate, survive and grow. Only thirdly and incidentally did it provide the only means of drainage that the mediaeval cultivator possessed. The furrows that lay between the ridges remain to this day on old Northamptonshire and Leicestershire pastures. Ewes and their lambs lie high and dry here on the mummified ridges while the spring rains accumulate in the furrows beside them; so did the mediaeval farmers' wheat and barley and oat seed lie dry above the sodden closing furrows drawn out by the weary ox-team. It is, however, important not to underestimate the earth-moving ability of the plough with share but no mouldboard. Current work by H. Jordan Hine at Cambridge on the reproduction of early cultivation techniques is showing that in skilful hands a ploughshare alone will break ground up very thoroughly, but will not, of course, invert a furrow slice.

The substitution of the horse for the ox as an animal in the plough-team appears to have begun in the Île de France in the tenth century. M. Lefebure des Noëttes's theory that this was made possible by the invention of the stiff shoulder collar has been universally accepted; and it may well be so. He maintained that the mediaeval neck collar compressed the trachean artery of the draught horse under full load and interfered with its breathing, whereas the stiff collar rested upon the shoulders which then took the full burden of the draught. Like most horse gear and horse lore this invention came out of Asia some time after the decline of Roman power in central Europe, and it is likely that it was carried westward with the great folk movements of the fifth and sixth centuries. If Des Noëttes is right, then the use of the horse to pull carriages and implements for agricultural purposes moved west also at the same time. It appeared relatively late in Britain, but by the end of the twelfth century some of the more progressive ecclesiastical manors were using mixed teams of horses and oxen on their demesnes. Abbot Samson of Bury St Edmunds had a plough-team of six oxen and two horses on the light Breckland sands at Elveden in Suffolk, and the London abbey of St Paul's was using both a mixed team of four oxen and four horses and a six-horse team at Sandon in Hertfordshire.

This Sandon land runs from the clay-capped escarpment of the East Anglian heights down the dip-slope of the chalk to the greensand of the Vale of Baldock, and it is likely that the lay brethren who managed the farm varied the constitution of the plough-team according to the nature of the soil under cultivation. Oxen were far better plough animals for the heavier land, where a strong and a steady tractive effort was required. The horse-team was faster but less consistent in pull, and would have made a quicker and adequate job of ploughing the thin soils over chalk. It was this difference in the draught characteristics of the two animals which dictated the choice of one or the other where both were available; but for the peasant plough-teams it was rarely that horses were available, and their 'oxen' were usually the many-purposed cows which pulled the plough, filled the milk pail and bred a calf for sale. Historians have tended to acclaim the introduction of the horse into common use on the land as a major advance in agricultural techniques. It was nothing of the sort. For field work the ox was a perfectly satisfactory animal, and in a peasant economy its advantages over the horse out-weighed its disadvantages many times over. A change from ox to horse as the main team of the plough was progress only in the eyes of those who believed that the new was, *per se*, pro-gressive.

The pages of the contemporary agrarian manuals and of the modern agricultural histories are full of another obsession: that the skill of the husbandman lay in the repetition of cultivations, that the man who ploughed his fallows four times was a better farmer than the man who ploughed them only twice. This was often a fallacy and, in a dry season, must have robbed many a spring-sown crop of much-needed moisture. It cannot be known how far the advice of the farming theorists was regarded by practical men; often, probably little. These theorists produced, on the Continent, a stream of advice that continued, and usually plagiarized, the Roman agronomists. Probably ten per cent of it was sensible and useful, and ninety per cent either useless non-sense or positively harmful. The English mediaeval farmer was somewhat better served because the lack of continuity with Rome led to a fresh, and late, school of agricultural writers who wrote more from practical experience and less from much-borrowed theory. They advocated a perfection of practice, both in farming techniques and in land management, that may rarely have been attained but which had been empirically proved in the field. These men—Walter of Henley, Bishop Grosseteste and half a dozen anonymous authors—complement and colour the penny-plain picture of later mediaeval farming in Britain which can be reconstructed from the dry bones of the accounts and surveys of the period. These abound in the record offices, and show how the improved Continental techniques had been brought in and applied to the estates of the innovators while peasant farming was still largely hamstrung in practice by the communal open fields—but was freeing itself, by economic pressures, from the more tedious and servile of its obligations.

These economic pressures were the contemporary peak of the graph of the cycle which varies between an excess of labour on the land and a shortage. A previous peak had forced the late Roman landowner, when the sources of his slave labour ran dry, to let off large parts of his estate to tenants. The same sort of situation recurred in Western Europe in the fourteenth century when a population which had increased so rapidly as nearly to reach saturation point in subsistence was so drastically reduced by plague that where there had been too many people to be fed from the limited resources of mediaeval agriculture, there were now too few to farm the land. There were, indeed, so few that the manorial lords were faced with a grave under-supply of labour, with all that implies in bargaining power and a spirit of independence on the side of the workers. The Black Death in the 1340s was merely one, but the worst, of a series of outbreaks of bubonic plague that were endemic through the century. Before then, such had been the growth of population that too many men were seeking to cultivate too little land; after the plague, by the end of the fourteenth century, there was too much land and too few men to tend it. In consequence, landowners everywhere were forced to accept rent in cash instead of rent as labour from their servile tenantry; so that they had either to take in hand the holdings vacated by death or let them for money rents to men who were moving upwards in the ranks of freeholders.

Neither of these was an entirely new situation. The remission of labour services for cash had been proceeding steadily for centuries. Free tenants had long been putting holding to holding and reclaiming new land from wood and waste to make for themselves sizeable ring-fenced farms subject to none of the disabilities that attached to the collections of small strips and precarious grazings that made up the servile villein's little farm. And other landlords—notably the great monastic corporations—had been gathering holdings into their hands, and even forcibly depopulating villages, to provide elbow-room for their ambitious arable and stock-farming ventures. The fourteenth-century epidemics dealt a death blow not only to a large proportion of the population of Europe but also to the viability of the manorial system. The complexity of communal fields and of legal rights and obligations, and the servility of personal status took an unconscionable time to expire. These reached maturity in England in the twelfth and early thirteenth centuries, declined in vigour even before the visitation of the plague, but lingered on into senility over many centuries.

Commercial, as opposed to subsistence, agriculture received a great fillip from the loosening of the restrictive manorial bands. Pioneers had long been pointing the way to production of food for sale. We must dwell on these a little, because they prepared the way for the yeoman farmers who were the pride of the first Elizabethan England and for the great body of substantial husbandmen who succeeded them to the present day. It was particularly in livestock that the large states expanded most. The cathedral priory of Canterbury carried out extensive reclamation of the East Kent marshes to make pasture land for their dairy farms there, and in 1322 flocks totalling 6,000 ewes were being milked after the weaning of their lambs to produce upwards of 50,000 gallons of milk a year worth a halfpenny a gallon. Each of the bercaries had its wooden or stone-built dairy equipped with strainers, settling pans, presses and churns for making butter and cheese. If the priory made cheese alone, it could have marketed more than twenty tons a year. These 6,000 ewes were by no means all the priory's sheep at this time, for elsewhere in south-eastern England it had 8,000. Again, the abbey of Crowland mustered 11,000 sheep upon its lands, many of which were fenland grazings. Upon the dry hills of Mendip and the marshes of Sedgemoor the great abbey of Glastonbury in 1252 possessed 7,000 sheep and 1,400 head of cattle. Everywhere landowners with wide acres were seeking to raise their stock numbers to the full carrying capacity of their land; when the abbot of Ely surveyed his demesnes in 1277 he estimated that he could increase his livestock to 300 cattle, a breeding herd of 460 pigs, and 6,020 sheep.

The development of large-scale livestock husbandry was not the prerogative of monkish magnates. One layman at least, Henry de Lacey, third earl of Lincoln, applied very modern methods of commercial expansion to an unpromising area of Lancashire moorlands and turned them into ranches for the breeding and rearing of cows and working oxen. In 1295 he had twenty-eight moorland farms turning out cattle for sale. He worked them in conjunction with summer lodges on the higher moors to which stock and herdsmen were moved for summer grazing. Each unit of seventy-five to eighty head of cattle—thirty-seven to forty breeding cows and a bull, and the remainder young rearing steers and heifers—was let on a share-cropping basis to cow-keepers. Cows for sale were drafted to a market unit, and special oxen-farms served as transit and holding units whence stock were moved into markets at Bolton and Pontefract. Each farm was well-equipped with a cattle byre eighty feet long, to house what were probably the mediaeval ancestors of the Lancashire long-horns from which, centuries later, Robert Bakewell drew the foundation animals for his famous essays in livestock improvement. Eastwards, in the Peak, the earls of Chester also engaged in commercial cattle production. For their breeding centre at Macclesfield supplies were driven from Wales: records remain of purchases of sixty-eight at Ruthin and Abergele in 1347–8 and of seventy-five, mainly from the Bishop of St Asaph, eight years later. From the Macclesfield centre stock was dispatched for sale at the big north-western fairs; but even so, there remained at the end of one year—1356—166 breeding cows, together with 281 head of young stock being reared to the point where they could be taken into the breeding herd or sold.

If the records had survived there is little doubt that these mediaeval factory farms would be found to have existed in considerable numbers. Their promoters deliberately assessed the market needs and developed their latent resources in land to meet them. This was a long way from the subsistence farming of earlier days; and not only of earlier days, for around them there was the vast army of peasant-cultivators struggling to grow the food to keep starvation at bay, and not always succeeding. One of the main reasons why the fourteenth-century plagues took such a heavy toll was the malnutrition from a subsubsistence agriculture. It is probable that this was most acute in regions where the population was densest—often denser, indeed, than it is today. East Anglia in particular had a precocious development. Norfolk contained some 95,000 people in 1086, Lincolnshire 90,000, and Suffolk 70,000, an average of between forty and fifty inhabitants to the square mile, ranging from eighteen in the thinly populated Breckland to over eighty in the most favoured parts. These numbers had probably trebled or quadrupled by the eve of the Black Death, so that the pressure on land was such that a bad harvest was a mortal occurrence. Kosminsky calculated that in some of the most thickly settled areas here two-fifths of the villein holdings were too small to give a family the barest means of support in a year of average crops, and of the growing army of freeholdings three-fifths could never have fed their owners.

This intensity of habitation was no purely English phenomenon: it was replicated throughout all of Western Europe that was habitable. The pressures drove desperate men to take cultivation into parts that have now been long abandoned again to the wilderness—up into Alpine valleys, Welsh mountain-sides and the unrewarding granites of south-western England and western France. In the process the perimeters of cultivation around each nucleus of settlement were thrown outwards until they met; and the wastes disappeared. Hoskins has written of the Domesday scene that if one walked a mile at the most out from the village, one came to the edge of the wild, the frontier of unreclaimed country that extended to the point where the fields and grazings of the next village began; and in the Midlands and the Kentish weald the great forests were 'shedding and renewing their leaves with no human eye to notice or human heart to regret or welcome

75

the change'. Two hundred years later, lowland Britain was largely one field full of folk, and even the most barren soils had their peasant ploughmen to pour out their sweat upon. The now famous deserted villages, not only of England but of France and Denmark, in the Alps and in the *wüstungen* of Germany, were the high-tide marks of an advance of peasant and seigneurial agriculture in the attempt to fill hungry stomachs; and when the stomachs of their owners were no more the tide of cultivation receded, leaving a fading signature of occupation behind in the ridges and hollows of remote fields that now mark where houses, churches and village streets once were.

But most of the newly won farms endured. Those settlements that were planted in former woodland in the twelfth and thirteenth centuries often bear tell-tale names: the many Woodhouses of Nottinghamshire stand where oak and ash once reigned unchallenged, and any place-name compounded of 'wood'—the Woodhalls for example—bears the same witness. Likewise the multitude of 'New' names—Newhouse, Newstead, Newton—perpetuate the foundation at this time of a new community of cultivators. The plough or the grazing beast was taken not only into the dense forest but into the marsh and the fen as well in these expansive centuries. Around the Wash and up the Lincolnshire marshes banks were thrown up to contain the sea; and as the land dried behind them and the salt content of the soil diminished new grazings were taken in. Sometimes this reclamation was the work of landowners with large resources, notably those great early improvers, the Cistercian abbots; but often it must have been accomplished by the co-operative labours of the villagers bordering the marshes. These mediaeval intakes are now some of the best-used farmland in Britain. The great holdings of the agricultural company of Strutt and Parker on the Essex marshes and the 7,000-acre farm of Raymond Caudwell at the significantly named hamlet of Marsh Chapel in north Lincolnshire (where the street runs on top of the thirteenth-century seabank) are two of the most productive agricultural empires in the mid-twentieth century. Their land was won for them, yard by yard, nearly blade by blade of grass, by the communal reclamations of long-forgotten peasants, either hungry for lack of acres, or hungry for more acres upon which they could practise the first beginnings of an industrial agriculture.

Towns were becoming a commonplace of the English scene, and the burghers bought more food than they grew. So, as the older generations of farming townsfolk died out and their open field plots passed into other hands, the new urban dwellers looked to the market-places for their provisions. The exact nature and extent of this growing commerce in foodstuffs are not known; but the urgency with which many thirteenth- and fourteenth-century magnates founded new towns or expanded old ones and paid the royal exchequer for the privilege of the monopoly of a market indicates beyond doubt the profits that lay in these ventures. The abbot of Westminster, who was the lord of the manor of Stevenage, at whose pattern of open fields and freemen's farms we have already looked, probably quite deliberately encouraged the change in focal point of the settlement from the church, which lay secluded half a mile off the Great North Road, to the road itself, which was growing in importance. The plan of the new village which developed in the twelfth or thirteenth century plainly centred upon a wide market-place; and for the holding of the weekly market and the annual fair Westminster bought a charter from Edward I in 1281. The same pattern was repeated all around: six miles to the north of Stevenage the Knights Templar actually founded a new town at Baldock in the corner of one of their manors in north Hertfordshire, and laid it out around a market-place. At St Albans, fifteen miles to the south-west, its abbot carried through a most ambitious piece of urban and commercial planning on similar lines.

The ultimate objective of these reverend fathers in God may have been the greater glory of the Lord; but the immediate aim, and the one that was foremost in men's minds, was the increase in manorial revenues that came from rents and court dues and from the substantial tolls levied upon the market transactions. The national economy was suddenly growing up, and it nourished itself mainly on the one commodity which stood in importance above all others, the surplus food from the land. This fever of urban speculation was nationwide: it stretched from Woodstock in Oxfordshire to Portsmouth, from Liverpool to Plymouth, from Stratford-upon-Avon to the pristine town of Salisbury, newly erected by its bishop in 1220-25 two miles south of Old Sarum. As population expanded, more and more land was reclaimed to feed it, and as the supply of foodstuffs grew so it was possible for an urban civilization to develop which, outside London and one or two other centres of international trade, depended upon the tide of commerce between town and country. It is no accident that market towns lie half a dozen miles apart throughout lowland England. This was the basic unit of distance, similar to the architect's module, at which centres for the sale of rural produce lay most conveniently for the men and women to carry in their butter and drive their lambs, and cart what surplus grain they had. It was also the distance most convenient for the owners of the markets—for all markets, like all land, are owned by somebody—neither too close so that one centre might harm a neighbour's trade, nor too distant so that the business was lost between two market stools.

As in agricultural techniques, so in this encouragement of an adolescent urban-rural economy did the country magnates of England and the Welsh and Scottish landlords look to the Continent for precedents. France and the Rhineland had gone this way decades and centuries before; or had never wholly lost the Roman mercantile pattern. One process that seems not to have been borrowed from Europe was the much-used Continental system of reclaiming whole new regions by the planned settlement of peasant cultivators in them. The Romans may have employed it to open up the fenland of East Anglia, and William the Conqueror may have brought some wasteland in the north into use in this way. But there is nowhere in the English records a plan to match the clearances in North Germany, where colonists were imported from the Low Countries by an agent who was little less than a contractor employed by the landlord to direct the operation. Likewise, in France, much of Brie and Entre-Deux-Mers and some of the land of the Abbey of Saint-Denis were let to pioneering tenants. In all of this, the old manorial obligations of week-work and boon-work and carrying services would play no part: the settlers were tenants for cash; and where such a

high degree of freedom was being gained the servile tenurial
system in Western Europe, already far decayed, was doomed.
No such examples were at hand to hasten the end of villein
obligations in England, where it was left to the accretion of small
local pressures over centuries and then such calamities as plagues
to introduce, very gradually, rents in money and leases for terms
of years or for several 'lives' (or generations) of a family, in place
of a servile tenancy at the whim of a manorial lord who was controlled only by the degree to which he was obliged to regard the
custom of the manor.

Nonetheless, despite the apparent absence of plantations of
free tenants charged with the task of turning virgin forest or wild
moorland into agricultural holdings, the face of the British lowlands was being shaved and scrubbed clean by the very intensity
of the existing settlement until the fourteenth-century degenera-
tion set in. There was rarely land to spare for the needs of
expanding villages; often, not nearly enough. Such wastes as
there were—in the drier valleys of Wales, upon the Yorkshire
moors, in the drainable marshes, in the kindlier areas of Scotland,
in odd parcels of woodland which the accidents of habitation had
left uncleared—were, more often than not, acquired by the
pioneering orders of monks. It is difficult to over-rate the work
of the Cistercians in particular in developing the unused or
under-used lands which were given them so freely by those men,
from king himself to the lowliest knight and humble proprietor,
whose souls felt the need for intercession in heavenly places. A
highly organized system of granges was evolved, where lay
brethren worked the holding under the control of the official of
the abbey charged with the supervision of its estates. My own
land is a handy example. It was given to the Cistercian abbey of
Warden in Bedfordshire in 1150 by the third generation of
quarrelsome, fearless and murderous Norman owners in an effort
—no doubt fruitless—to enter into Paradise. Upon it the monks
erected a substantial farmstead built of stone carried by pannier
or cart from a quarry thirty miles away. They maintained a small
working staff of lay brothers upon the grange, which also served
as the centre for operations and crop storage for other small
pieces of land around, some of them given to the abbey by small

freeholders who could scarcely have differed except in legal status from their villein neighbours. The next grange lay four miles to the north, and between it and the abbey there lay a chain of several other granges. The produce from all went into the abbey's home barns, and thence to feed the abbot and convent or for sale. All the abbey's lands appear to have been cultivated and stocked intensively and managed by commercial methods quite foreign to the villein tenantry of local villages owned by laymen; and they continued so until the problems of manpower that arose in the fourteenth century forced the abbot to withdraw from the personal use of his remoter possessions and to lease them to local freeholders. So Bradfield Grange came into the hands of one of the rising class of yeomen whose descendants were still in occupation when Warden Abbey was dissolved by King Henry VIII. In the meantime, by the terms of one of the fifteenth-century renewals of their lease, the yeoman Newports (now substantial landowners) had rebuilt the old grange in the new enduring fashion, and left it to stand firmly to the present day, a solid and dry and apparently indestructible farmhouse. It is only four links in the chain away from the Saxon thegn who lived here on the day when King Edward the Confessor was alive and dead.

The first mediaeval grange that stood here may not have been dissimilar to another lay brothers' house recently investigated on Dartmoor by Lady Fox. This pastoral steading, in use at least from 1250 to 1350, comprised a two-roomed house twenty-seven feet long and twelve feet wide inside, which was joined by a walled yard to a byre measuring forty-nine feet by fourteen feet internally and containing pens and a stall for cattle, sheep and a horse. It is recorded that up to the time of the Black Death the abbots of Buckfast were accustomed to send a lay brother and a herdsman to look after their stock on Dean Moor, and this was certainly the grange where the lay brother slept in the house and the stockman in the byre, which had a hearth. The house appears to have been solid and not uncomfortable and it was probably of the standard to which the middling peasantry of the thirteenth and fourteenth century were accustomed. The many excavations of deserted mediaeval village sites that are now being carried out will certainly add much to our knowledge of rural

Welsh longhouse at Llanerch-y-Cawr

Tallet at Black Hill, Herefordshire

Brown Swiss cattle

homes of this period: it could scarcely do otherwise, for virtually nothing has been known hitherto. It is likely that the peasant houses will be found to have been better than the hovels with which the small mediaeval farmers have been associated in both the popular and the professional historical mind.

This may also be true of the houses of the earlier Saxon period. As recently as 1948 it was written that their habitations were wretchedly flimsy. In the fifteen years since then evidence has begun to gather that this statement rested upon a misinterpretation of the excavations of the principal Saxon settlement so far investigated, that at Sutton Courtenay in Berkshire, where the hovels that were identified as houses may have been merely the worksheds of weavers and other craftsmen, and that if anyone slept in them they were only the slaves. It is more likely that the family (in the widest sense) of the Saxon agriculturists of some substance lived in longhouses that were both capacious—for the human beings at the upper end and the livestock at the lower—and substantial; and similar to the longhouses, described above (p. 43), which were the European houses of the ancestors of the Saxon settlers in England. The one royal Saxon palace which has been excavated, at Yeavering in Yorkshire, was merely a superior and elaborated version of this type of rectangular homestead; and Mr C. A. Ralegh Radford has suggested that in searching for the as yet unknown dwellings of the Saxon ceorls 'we must look for a rectangular building with an area of some 40–60ft by 12–15ft'. Neither the Saxon nor his late mediaeval peasant descendant lived in luxury—the inventories of the goods and chattels of the thirteenth- and fourteenth-century small freeholder list only a bed and a few pots and pans—but neither's home may have been as despicable as we have imagined. They stood more thickly than ever before in a countryside that, in the lowlands at least, retained little of its primitive wildness and few of the more fearsome of its wild creatures. The wolf still preyed upon defenceless men and beasts in times of want, and did not die out in England and Wales until the sixteenth century, or in Scotland and Ireland until the nineteenth. But the brown bear had disappeared before or during the Saxon settlement, except in remotest Scotland. Here, too, a few reindeer still lingered into the twelfth century, when the last of the British beavers was damming the Teify river in Wales, and the rabbit was a valued newcomer protected for the sport it provided the rural gentlemen.

CHAPTER FIVE

Yeomen and Businessmen

In Britain, the fifteenth and sixteenth centuries were notable
for two things: the emergence of the great army of yeoman
farmers who were to be the darling of the Tudor governments;
and the virtual disappearance of servility in the land—in practice,
if not always in the eyes of the law. For in 1586 even so great a
man as the mayor of Bristol had to be saved from the consequences of his hereditary villein status by the intervention of the
Privy Council; and as late as 1618 a Mr Pigg, otherwise unknown
to history, sought from the courts a declaration of his personal
freedom. But the irresistible force of economic circumstances
was working so consistently and so firmly against the feudal landlord that the effective agriculture of the country became the
profession of free men of substance and widening acres rather
than the occupation of unfree peasants on holdings subdivided
beyond the point of self-subsistence. Furthermore, events turned
the hereditary landowners nearly into a depressed class, and
placed all the advantages in the hands of the larger tenantry.

Many of the reasons for this volte-face have been touched
upon. The decline in population from famine and plague put
labour at a premium; and repeated legislation designed to limit
the mobility and the demands of the farm worker failed utterly
in the face of competition by two masters for one man. Com-
mutation of personal services for a money rent had proceeded
steadily over the centuries, and the calamities of the mid-four-
teenth century had compelled many landlords to abandon week-
work and the other forced labours of the servile tenant and either
to resort completely to a paid farm staff or to retire from demesne
farming altogether and become rural rentiers, leasing their lands
to their larger tenants or to newcomers. But rents were largely
fixed for long periods by copyhold leases for years or lives, and
inflation was in the air. In the event the smaller landowners

became the first of the long succession of gentlefolk in reduced circumstances, living on fixed incomes in a time of steady rising prices, who have always been the worst hit of the victims of a depreciating currency. The tenant farmer—the yeoman—on the other hand enjoyed all the advantages of a rent fixed at pre-inflation values and the sale of his produce at inflated rates. Little wonder that he became the backbone of rural Britain, a man with whom 'time has indeed dealt favourably . . . in diverse respects'. Robert Furse, the Devon yeoman, put it in the strong and vivid prose that flowed naturally from the pen of every Elizabethan: 'Although our progenytors and forefathers were at the begynnynge but plene and sympell men and wemen and of smalle possessyon and hablyte, yt have theye by lytell and lytell so run ther corse that we are com to myche more possessyones credett and reputasyan than ever anye of them hadde.'

The magnification of the yeomanry has led us on in advance of events. Perhaps the most significant factor in the emergence of a substantial class of land users was one which has already been suggested, the aptitude of livestock farming to commercial expansion in the particular circumstances of late mediaeval times. It fitted the conditions of the period for several reasons. First, it needs little labour; and in the late fourteenth and fifteenth century men were scarce and dear. Second, its products have a high value for their weight, for a pound of wool or meat or butter is worth far more than a pound of wheat; and therefore the cost of cartage took a less heavy toll on the producer's returns in a day when transport was slow and difficult. Third, the capital needs were less than those of an arable farm. And fourth and most important, it made profitable use of land which could not be utilized economically for other, more intensive agricultural purposes: dear labour, high costs, lack of a market, all put corn-growing out of court on the marginal areas, which have over the centuries slipped in and out of cereal cultivation with long-term movements in grain prices. Livestock farming was then, and continued to be for many centuries, an extensive user of land. Until intensive methods of livestock husbandry developed in the twentieth century, either on grassland made highly productive by artificial means or in farm livestock 'factories', the rate of stocking was very low except where pressures of rural population put pastures at a premium. In the fifteenth century the normal stocking rates on the grazings of the wolds or the chalk hills of southern England was probably a ewe to the acre or a beast to five acres—somewhere between three and five times less intensive than in the best modern practice. Finally, the grazier continued to find a profitable and certain outlet for his principal product, wool, when the market for food was unstable or non-existent. It was a commodity that was in a commercial and international demand that appeared to be insatiable.

The economic retrenchments that followed fourteenth-century famine and plague provided one set of conditions that took sheep farming out of the general run of land use and gave it a long-enduring pre-eminence. It was no innovation: sheep had fed on British pastures for three thousand years, often in numbers that dwarfed the human and other domestic animal populations. Throughout mediaeval times the flock had filled a place of importance in seigneurial and peasant economies. The Domesday returns for the counties for which livestock figures survive indicate how comparatively thickly they stood upon the grazings of the demesnes: upon the thin, blow-away sands of the Norfolk Breckland there were 4,500 sheep on the demesne lands of five manors, there were more than 1,600 on three manors on the Mendip hills in Somerset, there were 2,850 on seven royal manors in north Devon. The whole county of Norfolk had 46,000 sheep on its demesnes, and since the peasant flocks were probably even larger the sheep population of the country may well have approximated to that in 1937—112,000—before the reduction in stock during the Second Great War. To the south, Essex may have had more than 90,000 sheep in 1086—and only 78,000 in 1937. So few records of peasant flock sizes remain that it is not possible to assert categorically that they exceeded even the seigneurial flocks, but the stray pieces of evidence suggest that this was so. On the bishop of Winchester's manor of Merton in Wiltshire the eighty-five tenants had more than 2,500 sheep between them. The danger of under-estimating the worth of a peasant tenant is exposed in this same village: Rudolf Truhe was to all appearances merely the villein holder of a thirty-acre virgate and the widow

Matillis a poor smallholder of fifteen acres—yet the taxation returns for 1225 show that the first had 158 head of sheep and the second sixty. There is no reason to suppose that these villages on Salisbury Plain, with their short sweet grasses on the uplands and their rich valley meadows, were untypical of the ancient sheep countries.

Sheep were, therefore, no strangers to the British countryside before the great centuries of wool production; and when the manorial demesnes were put out to farm in the fourteenth century there were affluent and ambitious peasants at hand to lease them, stock them, and turn yeomen. They were quickly joined by urban men of commerce, for at no known period in British history has a majority of successful townsmen failed to replant their rural roots and turn squire, with one foot under the manor table and the other muddy from the fields. As wool prospered in the fifteenth century John Tame, wool merchant of Cirencester, expanded typically. In 1480 he set up as flock-master on great extents of grazings around Fairford and died leaving bequests to four head shepherds. These were lands from which the old pattern of manorial demesne and villein tenantry, of feudal burdens and communal cultivations to the very edges of the waste, had virtually disappeared, and the new fashion of extensive yeoman or squirearchal farming had come in.

As in so much else in rural business, Europe led and Britain followed and overtook. The first great industrial ventures in Western Europe were based upon the manufacture of woollen clothes; and from the eleventh century Flanders, from Arras to the Scheldt, became an industrialized nation with a population that overflowed into Germany and other developing areas as land pioneers. Both this Flemish manufactory and the even intenser Italian weaving industry serving the great Mediterranean market were wool buyers, importers and processors, not wool producers; and the growth of the wool was left to the less developed countries where sheep husbandry had elbow-room and to spare. Principal among these were Spain and Britain, both supplying the superfine wools that the short hill pastures of the Welsh Marches, the Cotswolds and the Estremadura grew to a perfection that was reached nowhere else. Other regions of

86

Britain nurtured sheep that grew long wool, which was nearly as valuable as the short-woolled Lemsters and Merinos. The wool trade was one of international complexity, for a Flemish weaver might draw his fleeces from the Lincolnshire wolds, his dyes from India and the Baltic, and from them manufacture cloth for the garments of a rich merchant of Smyrna. It was obvious that in this intricate game of commerce the primary producers held the trump cards; and as soon as they chose to develop their manufactories and to process and weave their own wools they could starve the continental looms of their raw materials.

England in particular had long been building up its weaving industry, especially of the finer cloths of Stamford and Lincoln and the cruder homespuns of Oxford, Colchester, Marlborough and Winchester. But the bulk of the fine wools, many of them produced on monastic estates or collected by them from local small flockmasters, had been sold to Italian and Flemish buyers. The sheer force of economic development, rather than a consciously planned policy, changed the emphasis in the wool trade so that by the end of the fifteenth century the Flemish and Italian manufactories were in decline, partly from labour disputes and partly by the scarcity of and the export taxes upon their imported wools, and England was reaching the peak of prosperity of its weaving industry based upon its home-grown wool. Hitherto this had been concentrated in the towns adjacent to the great sheep-walks of the Cotswolds and Salisbury Plain, the East Anglian sands and marshes, and the Lincolnshire wolds. The invention of the fulling mill in the fifteenth century substituted for the trampling of the woven cloth by human feet the mechanism of water-powered mechanical beaters; and cloth-making went where the water was. The weaving sheds were moved out of the large towns that had been the focal point of the great flock-masters, and a rural or small town industry took root and grew prodigiously on the Pennine slopes, the Welsh border hills, the Cotswolds and the Mendips, the valleys of Devon, and the villages on the banks of the East Anglian rivers. It was now that the great cloths of Britain emerged: the Kerseys of the Stour valley in Suffolk, the worsteds of Norfolk, the Kendals of Westmorland and the friezes of Wales. And they were made by 'clothiers which dwell on great farms abroad in the country, where as well they make cloth and keep husbandry, as also graze and feed sheep and cattle . . .' and, it may be added, built the incomparable weavers' houses and the ecclesiastical masterpieces that grace the fifteenth-century villages and small towns.

The raw material of this, Britain's first important industry, came from the vast sheep flocks at which we have already glanced. The picture of the sheep husbandry of the time that can be built up from the surviving account rolls and surveys and from the agrarian treatises is one of efficient management, often on remarkably big-businesslike lines, and of competent techniques that—for the first time—appear to be the product of a native pastoral genius and not an adapted version of Continental practice. On the large monastic and baronial estates there was centralized control of stocking and breeding policy, of the collection and sale of wool, and of the treatment of disease; and the most suitable farms within a far-flung lordship became specialist units in the production line of fine wools—one would be the lamb-breeding centre, a second the rearing farm, and others kept the adult wethers from which the best and heaviest fleeces were clipped. During the period of the early growth of the industry of wool production—for it was nothing less—the leaders in output and in skilful techniques were usually the great monastic estates. On one of these, such as those of Canterbury cathedral priory, there could be 14,000 wool-producing sheep in forty flocks, or nearly 350 to the flock, with a staff of specialist shepherds from the head *bercarius* and the *custos agnorum* downwards; and yet the sheep enterprise would be only a part—albeit over a fifth part—of a great mixed farming 'empire' that is unrivalled even by the present-day agricultural imperialism of the most successful farmers. On the other estates, and particularly those of the Cistercian pioneers of the remote places and the scarcely less expansive Benedictines, wool was the greatest and often the only cash crop from the wide pastures. In the Cheviots, the flocks of the monasteries of Kelso, Montrose and Newbattle were about 10,000 strong, and in the principal monastic houses in Wales the flocks were nearly as large. Later, these ecclesiastical estates and the baronial estates of the Bohuns and Lancasters and Hungerfords fell victims to the economic pressures of the late fourteenth and the fifteenth centuries—as already had the arable lordships of the corn counties—and were gradually broken up among the rising class of yeoman farmer and merchant-turned-countryman. And it was these up-and-coming men who tended to join the older practices of sheep farming to the new and prospering trade of clothier. A great new middle class of rural entrepreneur was being born.

Despite our considerable knowledge of the commercial side of sheep husbandry, wool selling and cloth manufacture of the time—both in Britain and on the Continent—nearly nothing is known of the animal upon which the whole structure of these most important trades was built. A few deductions can be made. Dr M. L. Ryder has provided some clues by examining the parchments made from sheepskin which tell something of the size and type of wool and hair follicles which grew on it when it encased the late mediaeval sheep. And there is a handful of scraps of literary evidence. It is certain that types of sheep were now being bred for specific purposes. There were certain basic needs. A sufficient milk yield was important: to the great dairies making sheep's milk cheese for sale, to the peasant flockmaster for the sustenance of his family, and to everyone for the rearing of his lambs. It is likely that this milk yield was, at that time, larger than it is now, for breeders from the eighteenth century onwards have bred out much milk from the ewe by concentrating attention on body size, conformation and ability to mature and fatten early. But as the wool trade grew and the cow began to become a specialized dairy animal, the first requirement of the sheep came to be a good fleece. 'Goodness' in wool, of course, is a combination of many characteristics: length, colour, strength of fibre, absence of hair, degree of crimp, and lustre. Moreover, since different combinations of characteristics are needed for the many types of material for which wool is woven or used—from the finest textiles through felts to carpets—the definitions of quality are governed by the purpose to which the fleece is put. The character of the wool is mainly controlled by heredity: a breed or type of sheep will produce offspring which wear a similar fleece. But feeding may affect wool type considerably.

Short upland pastures produce a finer wool than does lush low-land grass, a chalk soil will harden the fleece, semi-starvation and exposure in winter will cause a break in the strength of the fibre and dim the lustre. The knowledgeable flockmaster of the fifteenth century was aware of all this and he displayed much expertise in maintaining the quality of his wool.

The finest wools came from the West Midlands and from a regional variety of short-woolled sheep that grazed the natural upland sheep pastures of Herefordshire and Shropshire. It was very probably just a fortunately placed and well-managed member of a great family of sheep types which had a common late pre-historic ancestor with the Welsh Mountain sheep that even today ekes out a bare existence on the hills of Cardiganshire, Plynlimon and the Snowdon massif. A combination of selection for a fine short fleece and a skilful control of grazing, with some housing in sheepcotes in winter, produced a fleece that was of a thinner fibre than any in Western Europe except that of the Spanish Merino. The great collecting centre was the now unimportant town of Leominster; and because of this the early Tudor writer was prone to describe this fleece in some such term as Lemster Ore. This quality of wool has been lost to Britain today by the short-sighted policies of such mutton-breeders as the notorious Robert Bakewell.

It is impossible to assign an origin to these fine shortwools. The probability is that they were descended from Bronze or Iron Age imports brought in by one or more of the waves of settlers. The regional variety that carried the highest priced Lemster fleece has been commonly called the Ryeland; but it is certain that any connection it had with the present-day Ryeland breed is remote. The same is not true of the great mediaeval longwool, the other principal type that brought so much profit to England in the heyday of her wool trade. It was probably not a coincidence that this sheep was found in the regions which centred upon the Roman provincial capitals of Cirencester and Lincoln; and it is difficult to resist the supposition that the Cotswold and the Lincoln sheep were, and are, descendants of the stock which Rome brought in to populate its great sheep walks. Both are large sheep, carrying an extremely long and heavy fleece, slow-maturing and not very prolific. The mediaeval and pre-Improvement Leicesters were very similar. All had high reputations as wool producers; their fleece were said to be un-equalled through Europe for fineness and strength in relation to their length, and there was some export trade in them; and the monastic houses in Lincolnshire which presumably ran this variety on the wolds filled twelve of the twenty-four highest-priced places in the valuation list drawn up by one of the leading Italian wool-buyers. All these large longwools have now outlived their day. They were designed by man through many centuries to fill one of the most important roles in the international wool market to the exclusion of nearly every other useful characteristic. They continued to flourish in a new role when large quantities of cheap, fat mutton were needed to sustain the heavy work of the labouring classes in the nineteenth century, whose strength and endurance came from animal fats and the starches contained in great gallonages of beer. The Improvers whose work coincided with the industrial revolution converted the longwools into heavy, well-covered carcases. But the modern taste, the modern house-wife, and the more sedentary nature of most modern work turned them into anachronisms of the animal world, and only a handful of them remain. One flock of Cotswolds alone survives near Cirencester; some flocks of Lincolns still provide large joints for the tables of Durham miners; the old Leicesters have nearly died out; and some of the longwools of the West Country, that moved to Devon with the weavers' mills, have managed to marry the old heavy fleece to a new, more currently acceptable type of small carcase. To all intents and purposes the glories of the mediaeval and Tudor wool trade have departed.

To Tudor governments, of course, the encroachment of the sheep on the countryside was frightening. They desired a reserve of manpower for defence—for 'shepherds be ill archers'—and a high measure of food production for a population which was rising steadily again; but, it seemed, the meek sheep was inherit-ing a too-pastoral earth, and land-hungry men were landless. The process of enclosure, which had been going on quietly for centuries, was removing the little scattered holdings in the com-mon field and the communal grazing rights and giving them to the ranching flockmaster; and much of the arable land of the ancient demesnes of the manors had been put under grass and sheep and was remaining there. The trend accelerated with the dissolution of the monasteries by Henry VIII and the redistribution of the land among the new order of climbing, ambitious collectors of acres—who came from a background of all the classes. Never, it was said, were there so many gentlemen and so little gentleness. Inevitably, the rising market for food eventually brought corn back into equal, and in time greater, profit than wool; but much of the land which was ploughed up again was now the enclosed sheepwalk of rural squire or yeoman. Men's minds went back to the imagined Utopia when England was filled with a prosperous peasantry, where now landless, rootless men were starving: 'the poore, selye, wretched soules, men, women, husbands, wives, fatherless children, widowes, wofull mothers with their yonge babes . . . what else can they doo but steale and then be hanged.' Rural unemployment had arrived again—it had been a short visitor in the thirteenth century—this time to stay for centuries. The Tudor sociologist inveighed against enclosure, against engrossment of land into a few grasping hands, against evictions of men to make place for sheep. The State legislated against enclosure, taxed over-large sheep flocks, endeavoured to control rural monopolies, and recruited the second eleven sort of landowners into a magistracy to administer the statutes for them. Unfortunately for the well-meaning but misguided legislators, these very men were the engrossers, the enclosers and the major sheep masters. Economic necessity, that irresistible force, was on the side of the new yeomen and the farming squirearchy; and against the utopians.

One solution was, however, propounded to the problems of rural unemployment and the extensive, industrial use of land as a wool factory: 'to make the proffitt of the plow to be as good . . . as the proffitt of the graisiers and sheepmasters.' It sought to flow with the tide, not desperately and hopelessly against it; and it caught at the modern notion of directing land use by financial encouragements and not Acts of Parliament and vain exhortation. To appreciate how opportune—in fact, inevitable—this new policy was, we must look at the markets for food that were arising throughout Europe. There are many estimates of the changes in population. One of the most widely accepted is that of M. K. Bennett, who has calculated that in 1300 the population of Europe was 73 million. By 1400 this had been reduced to 45 million by plague, bad harvests and starvation. Since then it has risen without a check: to 69 million in 1500, to 89 million in 1600, and to 115 million in 1700. In the two centuries from 1400 to 1600, Europe's mouths to be fed doubled. And two mouths could not be fed, two bellies filled, without a very considerable development in corn growing. So many factors are involved in movements of prices, wages and patterns of production that it would be ingenuous to suggest that it was a growing disparity between the demand for food and its provision that was solely responsible for the marked rise in cereal prices that occurred in the sixteenth and seventeenth centuries; but there is little doubt that this was the main reason. Governments blamed speculators, engrossers and all the other commercial felons in the Tudor criminal calendar—never the law of supply and demand. It was not until about 1650 that some sort of equilibrium between bread grains and population seems to have been reached in Western Europe, and thereafter the expansion of production in the French grain lands and to the east of the Elbe kept the balance either level or slightly depressed on the side of the cereal grower for upwards of a century. At the same time small beginnings in the improvement of farming techniques were made. To modern eyes these may seem to have been small, but they none the less represented an advance on the mediaeval methods which had continued little changed through the centuries of up horn, down corn.

These improving techniques were made possible by the removal of the shackles of open-field cultivation, by the growing civilization of the new farming community which comprised not villein virgaters but yeomen and small squires who had passed through the new grammar schools together, and by the surplus of cheap labour at call. As always in a boom, wages lagged behind prices; and the margins between the prices which farmers received for their produce and the cost of even an extravagant use of manpower were such that the land-proud yeoman could perform the operations of arable husbandry to a perfection that was hindered only by the weather and the tardy pace of his prime movers—oxen and small draught horses. Not all yeomen were land-proud, for rural authors inveighed against the undrained, weed-ridden farms of the procrastinators and the boors; but the beginnings of Victorian perfectionism were perceptible. Or so it seems. It is a curiosity of history that less is known about the arable husbandry of early modern times than about the agriculture which preceded it; and far less, of course, than about the farming of the eighteenth century which is embarrassingly well-documented. The great mass of ministers' accounts and other manuscripts that survives from the late mediaeval period illuminates the thirteenth and fourteenth centuries well enough; and in the later period the techniques of the Improvers and their disciples were discussed in print *ad nauseam*.

But for late Tudor and Stuart Britain there remains little beyond a few farming diaries, the inventories of the possessions of squires, yeomen and husbandmen newly deceased, and the writings of the agrarian polemists from some of which neither time nor plagiarist has succeeded in deleting the advice upon the management of elephants and olive groves—subjects of remote interest to north temperate agriculturists. In England, old Thomas Tusser's staccato doggerel probably came as close to agricultural reality as anything in print; but even he versified counsels of perfection and not the average practice. None the less, there are contained in his stanzas the elementary facts of his day—he published between 1557 and 1573; many of them were borrowed from the first substantial agrarianist, Fitzherbert, thirty years earlier. Fitzherbert was the first English author to distinguish cereal varieties and their qualities—six wheats, three barleys and three oats. He discussed elementary weed control. He analysed the regional types of plough, including the earliest reversible plough—from Kent—of which there is certain knowledge; and he described their construction in some detail and their setting to produce the type of furrow required—seed, stirring or broad. But despite the advances in agricultural finesse which he itemized with modern precision, his workers on the land, men and beasts, still sweated and toiled in the ancient ways.

94

The man raking after corn harvest still did so by means of 'a great Rake with yron teeth, made fast about a mannes necke with a string and so drawne up and downe the lande'; and the ox, pulling the ox harrow built of six two-yard long timber baulks set with iron tines, which proceeded staccato 'by twytches', had 'never been wo tyll he to the harowe goo.'

Tusser's rare earthiness and memorable pungency were rooted in the East Anglian arable farming practice of the middle of the sixteenth century; and even in so short a period as that between the two men it is possible to distinguish advances in practice which three decades of boom prices, enclosure and expanding education had produced. That this was a period of development in arable husbandry more rapid than ever before seems likely. Tusser virtually began the tedious discussion of rotations which continued for nearly four hundred years. When he advocated a four-course of barley, pulse, wheat and fallow on enclosed land it was a measure of the distance arable husbandry had progressed from the mediaeval two-field course of cereal—fallow. His manurial treatment was followed until the advent of artificial fertilizers. His hand tools were those of the early Victorian farmer: the spades for cutting and cleaning ditches and for peat, with the names that still come naturally to old country lips— skuppat, skavall and didall; the scythes with their cradles; the twitchers for ringing pigs' noses; the rick ladders and the threshing shovels. A countryman of 1800 would have felt little of a stranger in Tusser's East Anglia of the 1550s. The homely glimpses of the intimate daily routines of sixteenth-century farming, the aphorisms that have passed into common speech, even the careful observance of the moon's influence in such operations of husbandry as the service of a mare or the broadcasting of beans, all establish a familiar link over the centuries between Elizabethan England and the England of our grandfathers—or even fathers. Defoe observed such men as Tusser's husbandmen at work in the fields; Constable drew just such ploughs as they used; and George Bourne's Bettesworth could have come straight out of Thomas Tusser's *Five Hundreth Points of Good Husbandry*, scarcely changed. At this level—that of the man in the wheat-field—there was a continuum from the emergence from

95

mediaevalism to the beginnings of nineteenth-century mechanization that it is impossible to conceive occurring in the turmoil of mid-twentieth-century development. These men's methods stood nearly still for four centuries. About them, of course, all was progress. The face of the British countryside was changing, but hardly as fast as the successful man's attitude to society. The expanding towns were offering new markets for livestock and their products. Prosperity was erecting new houses for the yeoman and small squire so fast in the few decades each side of the year 1600 that the rural middle-class homes of Britain were virtually all rebuilt.

It is not possible to support the thesis of a general advance in arable husbandry by figures of yields: such do not exist on a scale sufficient to be statistically significant. All that can be done is to quote some returns which illustrate the height to which expertise in cereal growing could rise in the late sixteenth and early seventeenth centuries. In Western Europe, Flanders and the Low Countries enjoyed an undisputed lead in agriculture at this time, as they had for a century or more before. It was here that convertible husbandry was reintroduced; it had lapsed with the passing of the Roman agrarian technicians and reappears a thousand years later. It was first applied in a primitive rotation of two or three corn crops, a year's cleaning fallow and then several years' pasture, mainly in the lands around Ghent. In the succeeding two centuries the arable grass rotation was next developed by the sowing of fodder crops in the fallow year, as a cleaning crop to be eaten off by livestock in the field: these could be spurrey, vetches or turnips. Turnips, indeed, are found as early as 1404 being grown as a catch crop near Aalst. Then, finally, the long grass break was replaced early in the seventeenth century by a short clover ley. By then, a century and a half at least before the time of that pseudo-pioneer, Turnip Townshend, and two centuries before the heyday of that skilful, arrogant publicist Coke of the Norfolk Four-Course, the farmers of the Low Countries had evolved a turnip husbandry and an arable rotation precisely on the lines of the eighteenth- and nineteenth-century English Improvers. Their reward in terms of cereal

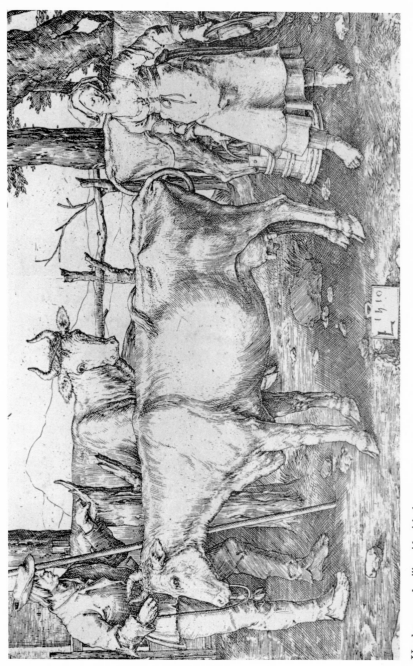

Herdsman and milkmaid with three cows

Dutch cow stable

yields could be remarkable: how often they were so, none knows. But in the years from 1570 to 1573 the Friesian farmer Reinck Hemmema, of Hitsum, was taking what can be calculated to be seventeen times his seed rate in yield at harvest, or—at the contemporary seeding of 1⅔ bushels an acre—a crop of about 30 bushels (16cwt) of wheat to the acre. This was about three times the yield that the well-farmed Winchester bishopric estates in England had averaged over three mediaeval centuries. The most reliable contemporary figures from Britain are from Loder's farm at Harwell on the Berkshire Downs where between 1612 and 1620 the average wheat yield was 29 bushels (15cwt) an acre, and the highest yield during these years 50 bushels (27cwt) an acre. This remarkable figure would have been a subject for boasting at a market ordinary in a southern England country town in the 1920s.

This, as has been said so often, was partly the result of the freedom of management of a man's own land which enclosure made possible. It was, in places, probably also the result of the land having been for long a heavily stocked sheep run, on which the accumulation of decades or centuries of manure and the fibre contributed by the roots of the pasture restored to full fertility soil which had been exhausted as continuously cropped and under-dunged open fields. But it was the enclosure that enabled a man to perfect his arable husbandry; and also to regulate his stocking, to prevent the disease entering his herds and flocks which it had been impossible to keep at bay on the common grazings, and to pursue a policy of livestock improvement which had been denied to him when his animals had pastured 'hoof under hoof' with those of other villagers. In this the English yeoman (the term is used from now on to denote the middling farmer, either owner or tenant) was more fortunate than his European contemporaries, who were still—and continued to be, —encumbered by their communal pastures. In much of Western Europe the system of village grazings was perpetuated by the villagers' own successes in maintaining their common rights against encroachment or complete appropriation by the landlords. In many places in late mediaeval days these rights were committed to writing on behalf of the association of common graziers—the 'mark' communities. Throughout much of Germany, Switzerland, Austria, France and the Netherlands both rights of jurisdiction and the control of many aspects of village life from Sunday observance to charities and education came to be added to the primary purpose of the mark—the administration and protection of customary rights in land—so that in time the mark became an authority which combined in one organization most of the powers enjoyed in England in later days by manorial courts, parish vestries and their overseers and churchwardens, and the lay magistracy. It is partly because the mediaeval organization of communal arable and livestock husbandry was vitrified in this way that much of Europe is still a hedgeless land without field boundaries, on which strip cultivation and the daily tending of stock at grass by the old men and women and the children are still pursued in the ancient ways. Britain, on the contrary, started to abandon communism in agriculture and stock husbandry almost as soon as it began to be practised. After the first centuries of initial settlement, land was reclaimed more often into private enclosures than as additions to the common fields. The aggregation of strips into privately held parcels proceeded slowly but steadily through mediaeval days. And plague, depression and the letting off of demesnes in the late fourteenth and fifteenth centuries accelerated the process of turning what was known later as 'champaign' into land 'held in severalty'. The loss to the peasantry was incalculable (in the exact sense of that word), the gain to the yeoman farmer was beyond value, the reward to the nation of a modernizing, rationalized and efficient agriculture was economically overwhelming (if socially debatable). All this time, and until today, the European peasant has been preserved as an anachronism and as a problem which governments are now solving painfully and expensively in order that their agricultures should become internationally competitive. The French peasant was embalmed by the mark; *laissez faire* let the English yeomanry expand and become technically competent.

The extensive English enclosures in the Tudor and early Stuart periods, the development of a commercial agriculture, the rise in population and the growth of markets all combined to produce a degree of rural affluence which was reflected mainly in what has been called 'The Great Rebuilding' of rural England, and parts of Wales. Comfort crept into the new homes in furniture, glazed windows, chimneys, featherbeds, and right down to the small household utensils which make up a great part of the inventories of goods and chattels which are attached to the middle-class wills of the time. But it was the sheer extent of house rebuilding which was the hallmark of the late Elizabethan and Jacobean countryside. This is strikingly evident even to this day to any saunterer through, say, the less spoilt villages of Warwickshire, Devon or Hertfordshire. Every other farmhouse or cottage can be externally dated by eye to this time; although internally, and often at the rear, the remains of one or more earlier buildings are seen to be incorporated. Outwardly, the owner kept up with the Elizabethan Jones to good effect in the architectural idiom of his region—if architecture is not too grand a word to use for such simple and homely exercises as inserting a floor and central chimney breast in an old halled house, or adding a cross wing to it, or even starting from scratch with a timber framework with the panels wattled and daubed and the exterior either left half-timbered or soon plastered to keep out the draughts which crept through as the daub dried out and contracted. In the manor houses, particularly in eastern England, brick came into use, often in pleasant ornamental forms and patterns of colour. On the Scottish border the building of tower houses saw French influence brought in to soften and elaborate the older Scottish baronial style. The half-timbered, often jettied architecture of the west Midland counties spread deep into lowland Wales and into Montgomery, Brecon and Glamorgan in particular. The yeoman homes blossomed into two main living-rooms, one on each side of a central chimney-stack, with the fire-places wide and deep for wood fires under a stone arch or massive oak bressummer; one or more best bedrooms over, where the farmer moved his bed from its ancient site in the parlour; a kitchen of some size; and usually an extensive range of rooms in which the products of the farm were stored or the housewifely arts of rural domesticity were practised. The brewhouse and the bakery and the cheeseroom, the lofts for grain and fruit, the wash-house and the dairy, the cider house and the place where the bacon was brined or salted in lead vats or on slate slabs are all found in rural homes of any pretensions. And in the larger farmhouses where much labour was employed this domestic and storehouse wing usually had a sleeping loft over for the unmarried men who lived in—as bachelor labourers still do in France and Holland and Germany.

The days in which a man's chattels could be numbered on the fingers of one hand when he died were also passing fast. A prospering yeoman could die wealthy in the material comforts of life. When the four 'appraisers' listed the 'goods Chattle Cattle manye napery utensells and houshold stuffe' of John George of Writtle in Essex in 1638 they found in his hall two tables, a form and ten stools, eight chairs, a clothes press, cushions and painted hangings, fire-irons, a musket and a 'birding piece', and five books. He had remained old-fashioned enough still to sleep in his parlour on a 'faire ioynd Bedsted' curtained and well furnished with bedclothes, and here also were another press, table and stools and chairs, a glass case with glasses, brass candlesticks and no less than 71lb of pewter plate. In the three bedchambers were four more bedsteads and a great variety of clothes and linen in the presses, cupboards and chests. A long list of kitchen utensils was headed by five brass kettles and five spits on which the meat was roasted. Adjoining were the brewhouse with four vats, a milk house, a servants' chamber and a room used for spinning. Outside, the implements of husbandry included five carts and a full set of harness for the four horses and a colt. There were only a few head of stock because this man was an arable farmer who had sown fifteen acres of wheat, eight acres of mixed oats and peas, fourteen acres of barley, peas and oats; and there were twenty acres of fallow in two common fields. With fifty-seven acres in all, he died worth nearly £400, the equivalent of £10,000– £15,000 today. Three hundred years earlier a villein virgater would have had a trestle table and a form on which to sit to eat his meal off plain pottery, and he would have slept on a straw pallet. Three hundred years later a smallholder of fifty-seven acres could have been less well furnished than John George, yeoman of Writtle, and not be judged poor in his possessions. That is a fair measure of the prosperity which encompassed an early seventeenth-century English farmer of modest acres. He had come, in the words of Robert Furse, 'to myche more pos-sessyones credett and reputasyan than ever enye of our pro-genytors had'; and his descendants over three centuries were scarcely to better them. The emphasis has merely moved. John George had few debts, some money on loan to friends and neigh-bours, and a great solidity of oak joinery around him. His mid-twentieth-century counterpart may have two motor cars, a large bank overdraft, an income exactly equivalent to the grants and subsidies the State gives him, and a television set. In real wealth and security at this level on the ladder of agricultural society there can be little doubt who was the more firmly founded.

The yeomanry was, of course, only one order in the farming community. Virtually everyone who lived in the countryside was occupied with the land in some way. At the top, the highest ranks of the nobility cultivated some part of their vast estates and many were vigorously engaged in estate management. The leading gentry were nearly completely occupied with agrarian affairs, and the minor gentry shaded imperceptibly into the yeomen: they were distinguishable often only by the possession of a substantial freehold while the yeoman was, by legal definition at least, merely a 'forty shilling freeholder' and often merely a copyhold tenant. Below came the husbandman, of whom the criterion was perhaps that he was himself engaged in manual labour for most of the day.* The gradations were subtle—as elusive as the dividing lines between the grades of middle class of today—and men constantly moved over the borderline from one stratum to another. 'A yeoman', wrote old Thomas Fuller, 'is a Gentleman in Ore whom the next age may see refined.' The yeoman and the husbandman shaded off into the tradesman so often that it was hard to define a man's principal occupation. Probably half the men in a village who were engaged in farming also carried on small businesses as innkeepers, millers or crafts-men, turning an extra penny into the family purse. The habit is by no means dead. In my own parish, as I write, two craftsmen who were morning and evening dairy farmers have recently

* 'though hee thriveth ordinarily well, yett he laboreth much.'

abandoned their paid occupations to become full-time farmers·
Higher up the Tudor and Stuart scale, cloth, iron and coal gave
larger yeomen and the smaller gentry great opportunities in an
economy that was on the threshold of its first industrial expansion. A small farming squire in Lancashire could talk of his
'coleryies', a Durham yeoman lease his coal rights, a Sussex yeoman sell off a thousand loads of iron ore, and in Yorkshire yeo-
man-clothiers were two-a-penny, their wool chambers crammed
with 'fleece wole and Keirsaye peecies' and their lofts furnished
with looms and 'walker sheares' while in the yard below were
their livestock and their implements of arable husbandry.

It was often the commercial, industrial outlook which this
duality of occupation engendered that also nourished the ambition to progress in agriculture and to expand in landed estate.
To men whose ambitions lay in acres the times were propitious.
The dissolution of the monasteries in the third and fourth
decades of the sixteenth century released vast areas of clerical
estates on to the market. They fell first into the hands of the large
landowners and the speculators; but these then divided and re-
marketed their bargains so that by the end of the century the old
monastic land was coming within reach of the small, farming
buyer. Many of the crown lands also came on to the market,
with the avowed purpose of raising money. Right down the chain
of social degree there was a fluidity in the land market on a scale
unparalleled before—and probably since only in the radical
changes of ownership that have taken place since 1919. In Tudor
and Stuart Britain, as now, it was the prospering middling farmer
who received the greatest benefit—comparatively so, that is,
because although others added to their estates, the yeoman then
was able, as have been the expanding army of owner-occupiers
in the mid-twentieth century, to enlarge his agricultural empire
twofold or more whereas the county magnate increased his by
only a small fraction. Large sums, large for the time, were paid
by apparently humble men: in 1610 Thomas Jacob, a Suffolk
yeoman, bought land for £2,001.

Much land was also taken out of the traditional systems of
tenure and let on long leases; leases for 99 years were most
common, and the oddities for 5,000 or 10,000 years turn up in

the records. The rents of newly let land rose continually and sharply, and at times approached a figure that would have been reasonable three centuries later: it is unlikely that the holdings in Ivechurch, Kent, rented in 1608 for 20s an acre, were let much more dearly in 1908. Arable farms in the eastern counties increased sixfold in rent from 1590 to 1640–50. In the Midland counties tillage land was leased in 1648 for eight or ten times the rent it had commanded a little less than a century before. Pasture more than doubled or trebled in value. Many heads were shaken at the folly of those who were willing to pay these prices; but history justified them for two centuries or more to come.

Figures of this order were asked, and taken, only for enclosed land: unenclosed land was worth less than half, often no more than a quarter, of the purchase price or rent or entry fine of the fields that had been taken out of communal use—by fair means or foul—and hedged. The fair means included agreed exchanges between strip holders so that a man's holdings in a common field could be brought together in one piece; or the action of the squire of a whole village in reorganizing the holdings into separate, integrated farms and buying out the lesser freeholders and the cottage owners of common grazing rights and a few small fields. The foul, though rarely illegal, means included wholesale evictions at the end of the year—a method employed by the most successful men of affairs, law or commerce to surround their vast and often vulgar new palaces with a thousand acres or more of parkland. The trend of consolidation of all sorts was most marked in the heart of England, the midland shires, where enclosure was to proceed on its controversial way towards completion only in the mid-nineteenth century. It was virtually absent from the perimeter of seaboard and border counties from Suffolk round to Somerset and up through the Welsh Marches to Lancashire, where such open fields as there had been had long before been divided and hedged. The likeliest reason for the difference between these areas of early enclosure and the open-field midlands is that the coastal districts of the east and south and the Welsh border counties and the regions abutting on to the Irish Sea were predominantly pastoral, while in the midland

103

counties from west Suffolk to Warwickshire and from Wiltshire
up to Yorkshire the plough was king.

Probably the greatest brake upon enclosure was the common
grazing rights which most villagers enjoyed over the arable
stubbles when the harvest had been cleared; and where the
parish or manor was mainly in tillage such rights of pasture were
jealously guarded, for other grazing for stock was scarce. The
incentive to put all suitable land under a corn crop, a result of
high cereal prices, put a further premium on the summer fallows
and winter stubbles of the common fields, so that a booming
corn market had the paradoxical effect of strengthening the
opposition of commoners to plans for enclosure. Unhappily for
them, the English commoners never had behind them such protective associations as the marks of Western Europe, and as their
resistance was worn down by the attrition of squire and yeoman
they succumbed to the processes of enclosure. But the cottager
and the little husbandmen continued to fight a rearguard action
against the quickset hedge over two or three centuries.

They were even less successful in fighting the encroachment
of the park wall. This was the age of what Dr Hoskins has called
'the flowering of rural England'—the great rebuilding of the
homes of prospering farmers from squire to husbandman. It was
also the age of the mushroom growth of the greater country-
house in Britain. Until the Tudor peace, the great men had been
residentially on the defensive, moated and embattled against
human predators as the more lowly homestead had been moated
against wolf and wild boar. Now, the strength of central government permitted them to relax; and prosperity—even sheer
profiteering from the opportunities which commerce, speculation, commercial monopoly or maritime adventure offered—provided the funds. Lord Treasurer Cecil's Burghley, Queen's
Sergeant's Phelips' Montacute, Bess of Hardwick's great Derby-
shire home, Knole and Audley End—'too much for a King,' said
James I, 'though it might do very well for a Lord Treasurer'—
were the greatest blossoms of this parvenu's high summer.
Around them, cottage settlements were destroyed or moved; and
a thousand or two acres were emparked and stocked with deer
and embellished with trees so that John Evelyn could claim in

his *Sylva* in 1664 that he had induced the great landowners of
Britain to plant many millions of seedlings and saplings. Both
the great parks and the lesser ones began indeed to stand out as
islands of afforestation in a land which had become denuded of
timber by housebuilding and heating, clear felling for reclamation, charcoal burning and the thousand and one other uses to
which Tudor England had put its woodlands.

Prosperity brought not only these things to the countryside—
stately homes, comfortable new houses, great parks and hedged
fields, grammar schools and pewter and feather beds. It also
brought 'country life' in its modern connotation: squirearchal
domination, an acquiescent clergy, a beginning of the gross dis-
parities of degree, priority and place, the landless and penurious
cottager, and the pleasures of the chase.

CHAPTER SIX

European Improvers

It is not easy to put a finger on the year, or even on the century, when science entered agriculture. It is no less difficult to define where empiricism in farming ends and scientific inquiry begins. Nevertheless, if one were to claim that the middle of the seventeenth century was the time, and an inquisitive interest by those who were primarily neither farmers nor agricultural landlords was the overture to the scientific approach, it would be hard to argue against these contentions. The transition from practice without science to practice with science—to borrow the motto of the Royal Agricultural Society of England—was not sudden. It came gradually. It came with travellers like Sir Richard Weston, who went to the Low Countries to find out what the best farmers did there, and why. It came with the new Royal Society when they initiated trials in 1662 into the growing of the potato. It came when such practising farmers as Walter Blyth expounded in his books on the English Improver—the first use of that pregnant word—the elements of the design of the mould-board of a plough so that it should not only turn the severed furrow slice but also press it firmly into place. It came when poor derided Tull applied the principles of the musical organ to a machine for drilling corn by releasing the seed from a central hopper through spouts into seed furrows. It came when horse owners developed methods of inbreeding and outbreeding their bloodstock so that Bakewell could borrow their ideas decades later for his work with cattle and sheep. All this, and much more, took place in the half century or so from 1650; and in Britain. It was at this time that England took a lead in agricultural development which she has never wholly lost—mainly, perhaps, because here the brake of peasant farming had been released from the wheel of progress. If you had turned to a man in, say, 1688 when Dutch William was landing in Torbay and had said to him 'Scientific farming has begun', he would scarcely have known what you meant; and if he had known he would have laughed at you, and denied it. He would, of course, have been right. It had not begun in the little fields of Devon around him; nor in the market gardens of Middlesex; nor on the sheep walks of the Yorkshire Wolds or the clay ploughlands of Warwickshire. But it had begun in men's minds, in London and in the manor houses of England; and from then on nothing could stop its arrival, long delayed though it might be, in arable field and pasture, in byre and barn. It was, perhaps, not until the late eighteenth century that most people realized that it was on its way; but the notions had been brewing for a hundred years and more.

If the decline of peasantry and the growth of squirearchal and yeoman farming were two of the causes of the development of British agriculture after the Restoration, another cause was certainly the continuing prosperity of this period in the countryside. The spectacular boom of the late sixteenth and earlier seventeenth centuries had subsided into a quiet and decent affluence and a better balance of reward as between employer and employed. This was in marked contrast to the Continent, where the high agricultural returns of the earlier period declined to a point which, if it stopped short of crisis, at least took on all the marks of a long-lasting depression. There, cereal prices fell and arable land was laid down to pasture, wages rose, and reclamation of the remaining wastes ceased. These regressions were partly caused by the Thirty Years War, the effects of which spread far beyond the areas involved in that conflict. A fall in the rate of population increase and a general loss of technical momentum, neither readily explicable, were other factors.

All over Western Europe the depression was reflected in the cessation of agrarian progress; even, at times and in some places, in some retrogression. In the century from 1650 to 1750 the reclamation of the Dutch polders nearly ceased because any land that was reclaimed could not be cropped profitably. Professor Slicher van Bath has traced the grassing down of tillage land—much of it exhausted from too-long continued crops with too little manure—from Germany, through Switzerland and the Jura, up through Burgundy and the Ardennes to Calvados and the north-western seaboard of France. The transformation from the diligently tilled cereal crop to green pastures reached its peak about 1720 or 1725, and such little depression as touched Britain occurred in about the same decade. But where the European transition from the plough to the hoof was born of a slump in the cereal market, that in Britain was rather the product of a return to a better balance in land use and rural production. The pendulum had been swinging fast—historically speaking—and violently: from the intensity of arable cultivation at the height of mediaeval population to the long post-plague crisis and a massive reversion to grass in the fifteenth century, then a rapid reverse in direction to the cereal boom of the sixteenth century. In the quietly progressive years of the late Stuarts and the early Hanoverians in Britain the pendulum fell into a gentler rhythm for a hundred years or more, with tillage and grass moving up and down in unexaggerated curves, until the militant era of the late eighteenth century, with its disturbance of international trade in feed grains, pushed the pendulum hysterically back into high cereal production once again; and the population explosion of early nineteenth-century industrialism kept it there.

This period from 1650 to 1750 in Britain, therefore, can be regarded as a time of natural economy in which land was not strained by being put to uses to which it was not fitted, and in which the balance between arable and grass, between the products of plough and pasture, was adjusted so that each could advance in techniques at a gentlemanly pace unstirred by ungentlemanly motives of excessive commercial profit. This was, indeed, the age in which the social aura of landed interest began to shine so temptingly to the mercantile classes, to the professions, and indeed to middle-class rural society itself which had valued its country property hitherto for its solid comforts, its income, its spaciousness and its sport, rather than for the unique status that its ownership conferred. Taunts of 'country boor' and 'bumpkin' could be heard at the London gaming tables; but sensible men knew that a Palladian façade standing in its timbered park, and a tenantry regaled in the steward's room as they paid their rents, and a private pack of hounds in kennel, and a parson or two also well to heel, were the most enduring and satisfying attributes of man this side of the grave. If this had been the whole extent of Britain's bucolic paradise no harm would have been done— except to the small army of displaced commoners—and a great deal of pleasure would have accrued to the privileged squirearchy. But there was more to it than this. The challenge of agrarian improvement began to prick the minds of many of the gentry of late Stuart and Georgian England—not necessarily as a means to profit but a finishing touch to the profession of rural living; the mark that set a gentlemen above the rank and file of country society and earned him a fame that could be more than local. It was also the product of a growing curiosity, of a fashionable philosophy of rural economy, of the application of proto-science to what was still the nation's greatest industry—agriculture. It was to the upper and upper middle classes pre-eminently, and to their preoccupation with improvement, that the first un-certain, largely empiric steps to raising the standards of the tech-niques and the tools of farming were due. Modern agriculture, both for Britain and for much of the world, was born in debate between an eighteenth-century Bedford or Norfolk landlord, his steward and his leading tenants. It is a far cry over two centuries to the economist with his computer and the chemist in his laboratory, who are the modern improvers; but the russet-coated gentleman with snuff on his waistcoat and powder in his wig was their progenitor. The phenomenon was largely British, but not entirely so.

Sir Richard Weston was the father figure of the breed. He was a Catholic Royalist, and in his exile in Flanders during the Commonwealth he studied the skilful methods of the Low Countrymen in growing clover and turnips, both well-established crops there, and on his return wrote of and practised his findings. After the Restoration the new rotations could be studied on his estate at Sutton in Surrey and read about in the several piracies that appeared of his *Discours of the Husbandrie used in Brabant and Flanders*. As the decades went by such gentlemen-authors proliferated—though not as fast as the new breed of hack writers upon agriculture, whose credulity, specious claims and gross inaccuracies gave rise to a suspicion of book-farmers which has hardly yet been lived down. But the gentry and the near-gentry wrote of what they knew themselves, or had done or seen. The Laurence brothers, one a clergyman and the other a ducal land steward, argued the economic and managerial advantages of enclosure; Sir Archibald Grant of Monymusk in Aberdeenshire reported the good husbandry of his noble neighbour the earl of Rothes; and Jethro Tull published in 1731 *The new Horse-Hoing Husbandry*, and had among his early disciples Lord Cathcart in Scotland and Queen Caroline herself in London. The fever of farming was abroad in high places. Robert Walpole read his land steward's letters first and his state correspondence next; and George II required the Tullian horse-hoe to be explained to him in detail. From Townshend with his eternal turnips to Bolingbroke sitting among the haycocks, the plough was divine and crop rotations were its prophets.

It would be tedious to follow the maze of literature, experiment and theory through these years. Ernle, Fussell and others have written of them exhaustively and well. They were the prelude, as it were, to the fascinating first act of the drama of agricultural improvement to be played later in the eighteenth century, with Arthur Young, William Marshall and John Sinclair as its critics. It would be misleading to suggest that the spirit of enlightened inquiry that was descending upon the most thoughtful countrymen was widely spread through all the strata of British rural society. Ernle long ago emphasized the distrust of innovation which kept most men to the well-worn paths that their fathers, and many generations before them, had trod. Tull himself wrote that if farmers were advised to sow clover they would certainly reply, 'Gentlemen might sow it if they pleased, but farmers must take care to pay their rents.' They equally distrusted those who sought to advise them; their retort to Bradley, professor of botany at Cambridge, was to ask him whether he himself could hold a plough, 'for in that they think the whole mystery of husbandry consists.' The attitude persisted. It was often justified, for agriculture has always had far more than its share of theorists and self-appointed tutors who, because they have once talked to a ploughman, deem themselves experts in the agrarian arts. It was sometimes unjustified; for hard and continuous toil, a lack of education, and the rural isolation that was unbroken before the motor car arrived, all combined to close mind and eyes and ears to all advice, whether it was good or bad. In the rank and file of early eighteenth-century yeoman, husbandman and hired labourer, ninety-five men out of a hundred clung obstinately to the old ways and refused either to listen to or consider the new; four might listen, but not act; and only one might accept advice and act upon it.

Many of the innovations that were to transform agriculture in the nineteenth century were already appearing. Oilcake as a cattle food was reported by Mortimer in 1707; the field cultivation of potatoes had begun in Lancashire; the ensilage of fodder crops was practised by a few. The two-furrow plough, a combined corn and manure drill, the egg incubator were all postulated. Turnips were accepted in East Anglia as a winter feed for stock, and Houghton reported the results of their use in his *Collections*, the first technical journal in Britain, probably the first in Europe; but most husbandmen rejected them without a trial. Only in livestock was some improvement made and accepted by the generality of countrymen—probably because the results of improvement were so patently self-evident. Breeding methods might be empiric; they could scarcely be anything else in the absence of a science of genetics. But empiricism had, over seventy or eighty centuries, changed the wild ox into a milch cow and the wild horse into a warrior's mount and ploughman's beast of traction, and the sheep from a hairy browser into a walking wool factory—and science has yet to prove that it can do very much better than that.

Scotland had already become a cornucopia of beef for England, and from all corners of the Highlands 'black cattle' walked to the great trysts of Crieff and Falkirk, thence to be driven south and fattened for slaughter, mostly on the pastures on London's northern dootstep. The bulk of the Scottish people themselves went meatless: as Smollett's Matthew Bramble said: 'Flesh meat they seldom or never taste'. Similarly, they went milkless, for the purpose of the cow was to bear and suckle the calves that, in the autumn of their fourth or fifth year, would begin their

long walk southwards, resting and grazing in hired fields overnight and avoiding, where it was possible, the toll-gated roads.
But by the middle of the eighteenth century a few Scottish
improvers were proposing dairy farming to their tenants, but
one of them, Grant of Monymusk, expected no more than 170
gallons of milk from a cow. Sheep, however, had scarcely begun
to signify in the Scottish economy: such as there were, were of
'an inferior naughty size'.

Wales, that other great reservoir of English meat, had a long
tradition of sending beef on the hoof westwards, and from the
fourteenth century onwards graziers had gone there to buy the
little, black-horned beasts for their pastures, or the tawny-red
sort of the southern Welsh hills. By the early eighteenth century,
if not earlier, the export of livestock from Wales changed its
nature. At first home weaving and then factory weaving encouraged a rise in the Welsh sheep population, and the English
market was an easy outlet for the surplus and aged stock. In
Snowdonia the transformation was most marked, and it was now
that the dry stone walls began to march up the mountain-sides
to divide flock from flock, and the massive sorting pens were
built with their entrances funnelled to the communal hilltop
pastures so that the sheep could be driven in for shearing, mark-
ing with each owner's sign, and drafting for sale. For this work,
which called for immense endurance in gathering the flocks, the
little black-and-white wall-eyed sheep-dogs were beginning to
be imported from the Scottish borders where they appear to have
been evolved. Their coming took half the work out of the gathering; but it seems to have taken nearly ten thousand years for the
symbiosis of man, dog and sheep to travel from its postulated
beginnings in the deserts of the Near East to the wet hills of
Wales. Gathered and culled for sale, the sheep and the black
cattle from Cardigan and Caernarvon were collected at Dolbenmaen, under the shadow of Moel Siabod, or at Tregaron beside
the great blanket peat bog. From there they were driven eastwards over ancient drove roads that marked out the course of
the later Holyroad road or the track that still wanders into the
valley of Abergwessin, to be dropped off among buyers in the
rich pastures of Shropshire and Herefordshire. The drovers

themselves were the nearest thing to men of business that Wales had yet produced, for they doubled the roles of bankers and commercial agents with their droving between the remoter Welsh counties and London.

The meat market in London—'the great mouth', Yarranton called it—was also supplied by some English stock, but less well than from Scottish and Welsh sources. In both these countries the beef animal was produced as such, and served no other purpose. Most English-bred beeves worked for a period at the plough, and connoisseurs of beef complained that this stunted them compared with the mature northern bullocks which were 'unwrought till they are fatted and killed'. This criticism was levelled particularly against the West Country beasts which were fed on the marshes of Somerset and the hills of Devon. These were mostly of the great family of red cattle which fringed southern England from the Wash to the Tamar; and they are represented today by the Devon, Sussex and Red Poll breeds. This type had been regionally distinctive for several centuries; and, together with the long-horned family of the western seaboard from South Wales to Sutherland whose descendants are the Welsh Black, the Galloway and the Highland, it formed one of the oldest strata of British bovine stock. The probability is that the red middlehorn of Devon type perpetuates the Celtic shorthorn of Bronze Age Britain and the longhorn of Highland type carries the blood of *Bos primigenius* of Neolithic sites and, through them, of the aurochs itself. It is suspected that there was some Roman importation of cattle, perhaps of the large, well-muscled white type that remains today in Italy; but there is no reason to believe that thereafter there had been any significant arrival of new bovine blood in Britain until animals from the Low Countries began to reach the eastern seaboards of England in, perhaps, the fifteenth century.

These Dutch strains, which themselves carried some of the blood of the massive Mediterranean whites, had begun to make their mark in the early seventeenth century by establishing in Lincolnshire and Norfolk a hybrid shorthorn which was the ancestor of the Beef and Dairy Shorthorn breeds of today. The indigenous half of the cross came from the ancient red family.

For yet another cross which was to play an important part in British livestock husbandry for some centuries, 'the Dutch Breed', as contemporaries called it, was put on a crossbred longhorn red type of cattle in the West Midlands and points north to make the Longhorn breed. These animals had an embarrassing length and curve of horns, so wide that they prevented their entry through a normal byre door, or so ingrowing that they had to be cut to prevent their piercing the beast's eyes. This Longhorn competed, over many decades, with the Shorthorn for pride of place in the production of both meat and milk—a battle which was not won till the mid-nineteenth century saw the decline of the Longhorn as perfected by Bakewell and the triumph of the Shorthorn in the hands of more enlightened breeders. The use of the Dutch breed on the old red stock of the Severn valley produced yet a third type of crossbred family, the white-faced Hereford; and a Longhorn cross upon these same reds bred the milch cows of the Gloucestershire breed. Later in the eighteenth century the Dutch bulls were also put upon an amalgam of southern Scottish types to manufacture the dairy breed of Ayrshire. The Dutch imports into East Anglia, and later into Kent, were therefore determining in the seventeenth and eighteenth centuries the future of at least half the types of British cattle that were later to stock the ranches and dairy farms of the world. It was the last, and the greatest, contribution of the Low Countries to the agriculture of Britain.

This first stirring of the revolution in livestock breeding among practical men was one of the exceptions to the blanket criticism that at this time the British farmer was a reactionary traditionalist who resisted innovation. In other fields of livestock the same spirit was manifest, but less adventurously. The raw material in the British sheep flock that lay to the improver's hand appeared to be more diverse than the cattle because, in pockets of isolation through the island, scores of varieties had developed which had only a local distribution. Many centuries of in-breeding and the effects of environment had combined to produce these variations —but they were variations upon no more than four basic themes. From Scilly up through the western islands to the Shetlands there was a horned, thin-fleeced, type that represented the sheep in its most archaic type: it survives today in the nearly extinct Loaghten of the Isle of Man, the Soay of St Kilda and, much crossed, in the very fine-woolled Shetland. This was certainly the original variety of sheep from an early prehistoric import. Second, there was a heath type that varied from the primitive sheep of the Welsh Mountains, best typified today in the last few Rhiw sheep that range the western uplands of the Lleyn peninsula of Caernarvonshire, to the shortwools that inhabited the west midland counties of England and which included the Herefordshire flocks that bore the fleeces that made the mediaeval wool of England famous. This characteristic 'Lemster' wool survived into the later eighteenth century, and specimens of the fleeces are included in the Bath collections of Wiltshire clothiers' samples. Third, there were the hairy-fleeced, heavily-horned and black-faced breeds of northern England. And fourth, the exotic longwools of Lincoln, Leicester, Kent and the Cotswolds, which may be the descendants of Roman imports.

In the early eighteenth century, the principal target of the British flockmaster was still the wool market; and only secondly came mutton and tallow production. The idea of a ewe as a breeder of fat lambs for the table was a novelty; and mutton was little more than a by-product of the wool trade. All this was soon to change, rapidly and radically, but as yet the sole concession that the national flock made to the gourmets' tables was in the use of prolific and early lambing ewes from Dorset to provide fresh winter meat for London. When Defoe rode through the south-western counties he was told in Dorchester that there were 600,000 sheep feeding on the chalk hills within a six-mile radius of that town. These were driven by the tens of thousand to the great fairs on the green at Weyhill, near Andover, and within the Iron Age ramparts of Yarnbury Castle, on Salisbury Plain. Here there also flocked graziers from all the Home Counties to buy both ewes and wethers to produce out-of-season meat for 'the great mouth'. The ewes were particularly valued for their ability to take the ram early and lamb before Christmas, often dropping twins. Almost certainly they owed these traits to an infusion of Mediterranean blood at some earlier date—perhaps a mediaeval shipment of Merinos from Spain or North Africa to some south-western port or an unrecorded Iberian settlement. Their descendants of today retain these same characteristics, with an ability to bear two crops of lambs a year. To a lesser extent, graziers on the famous Leicestershire pastures and in the marshes of Kent and East Anglia were also feeding sheep for the London trade; but their animals were of the larger local breeds and killed at mature ages, to cut into immense and often very fat joints for summer and autumn consumption at middle-class tables.

The pig served the humbler need of the husbandman and the cottager. By now it had ceased, or nearly ceased, to be an animal of the woodland, feeding upon acorns, beech mast and the roots which its snout was designed by nature to dig up; and it had become wholly domesticated, to live in the sty and hang dead from the kitchen beams. Some few regional types were discernible in the early eighteenth century. There was a prolific Berkshire breed which was doubtless the later distinctive red animal with black spots, in the process of manufacture from tawny swine of the Middle Ages, upon which imported black Chinese boars had been mated. There was a Welsh pig, of unknown type. And there was the 'Great Leicestershire Swine', as it was described by the Hertfordshire farmer-author Ellis of Gaddesden, which was fattened upon the pulse crops of the Midland farm. Already the beginnings of a complete remodelling of the ancient British pig were being made by crossing it with foreign stock. These imported pigs were described in 1732 as 'the small wild Black, China or West India breed', or as the Neapolitan pig. These were, in fact, varieties of the ancient eastern type, *Sus indicus*, with a long heritage of domesticity, a natural or acquired docility, and a prodigious ability to fatten. Hitherto, the British pig had evolved quite slowly from the hard-bristled, razor-backed, lean and savage animal of the forest which had been modified rather than radically changed by several centuries of selective breeding. The *S. indicus* cross was turning it into something that would have been called, a generation or two ago, a cottager's pig: short-bodied, fat, and as heavy in the shoulders as in the hams. The evolution of the modern baconer—long, lean and fine in head and shoulder—had to await the twentieth century.

The eighteenth-century cottage pig was admirable for its purpose: the production, over very many months, of the largest and fattest carcase possible, with great quantities of by-products for consumption while the sides were curing—the chitterlings and the black puddings, the haselet and the basins of lard, the brawn and baked pig's cheek and the scratchings, the fry and the liver cooked within the veil, the pluck, and the intestines carefully scraped for sausage casing. The cottage pig was the very ideal of Cobbett's cottage economy: nothing was wasted, and even the bladder became the children's football. The eighteenth-century countryman would have scorned the pre-packed, lean rasher of the modern supermarket; he would scarcely have recognized it as coming from a pig. True, a young and lean porker fed on whey, barley and beans in the Wiltshire dairying country could be found upon the delicate tables of the enervated townsman; but, Cobbett said, it would need 'a pretty hungry stomach to swallow it in Hampshire'.

In its livestock, Britain had yet no advantage over her Continental neighbours. Indeed, the Frenchman with his Merino sheep, the Low Countryman with his 'Dutch cows', the Italian with his pigs already much improved by eastern blood, and the Fleming with his great horses, all possessed farm animals of a type superior to any yet to be found across the English Channel. But the precocious industrialization of England was about to change all that, and in little more than a hundred years British stock would be flowing in a steady trickle through the civilized world. But before this revolution in animal breeding could be accomplished a revolution in rural economy and in the face of the English countryside had to be wrought.

Much has already been said about enclosure, that process of consolidating the open field strips, of dividing and fencing the commons, of putting the waste lands into fields. It had been going on in fits and starts for several centuries, sometimes slowly as when the communal agriculture of the Middle Ages was at its peak, sometimes fast as when extremes of depression or prosperity spurred men on to attempt to put their farming on a sounder economic basis. Paternal or apprehensive governments had continuously legislated and inveighed, but to little effect.

After the Restoration, government was synonymous with the landed interests, which had the strongest of all motives to put its estates into shape. Only a handful of literate peasants like John Clare, and of sociologists like William Cobbett, continued to argue nationally against enclosure. From 1760 to 1800, nearly $2\frac{1}{2}$ million acres in England were enclosed by private Act of Parliament; and in the next forty years another $1\frac{1}{2}$ million acres were enclosed in the open fields and three-quarters of a million acres of waste.

In about three thousand parishes in England, mainly in a broad strip running north-eastwards from Hampshire to Lincolnshire and especially in the east midland counties, the face of the countryside was completely changed. The mechanics of the business came easily to the governing class. The landowners of a parish caused a private enclosure bill to be drawn up and steered through Parliament. The enclosure commissioner then moved in, investigated claims to land or rights of grazing, and drew up a scheme for the equitable partition of the area among the valid claimants. Hedges and fences went up around the new allotments of land; old paths that had zigzagged around the heads of furlongs in Chestertonian insobriety disappeared, and new 'parliamentary' roads drove straight, or nearly straight, from village to village; and the commons and manorial wastes were split up. In less than a century central England was turned from a land of hedgeless open field strips and commons, interspersed with some fields of old enclosure, into the countryside of today with its uniform pattern of chequered green and brown and yellow, its hedgerows with elm and oak and ash towering above the pleached quick-thorn, and here and there the new fox-coverts of gorse or thick spinney which the hunting squires planted at strategic points. And new farmsteads sprang up in local stone or red brick in the centre of the consolidated farms.

This gigantic remodelling of million upon million of acres in the course of a few decades had many results. The least important, but the most pleasant, was the vast growth of the population of birds of the hedgerow. The most important result, in terms of human readjustment, was the disappearance of nearly all the remaining peasantry of England—the men and women who had

had an acre or two in common field strips, the right to graze a handful of stock on the common or the stubble and to cut firewood in the woods, and the opportunity to build a small hovel in some quiet corner of the waste. There was no room for people like this in the new rural economy. The most important result in terms of the national economy was the creation of a vast number of integrated holdings upon which the new farming could be pursued without the impediments and frustrations and quarrels of the old strip agriculture and the disease and mismanagement of animals on the overstocked commons.

The new pattern of farmsteads in the areas enclosed at this time filled the hitherto unpopulated stretches of land between village and village. Rural England had developed in two ways since the Saxon settlement. Those parts which are today the pastoral counties were either parcelled out in fields from the very beginning or enclosed at so early a date that all trace of the pre-enclosure pattern is lost. In these areas, of which Devon is the perfect example, the farmhouse had always sat in the middle of its land, reached by a winding lane and often throwing out farm cottages as excrescences; so that the rural scene has changed little. In the arable counties, at the other extreme, the arrangement of open fields and commons did not allow for the insertion of dwellings and byres and barns into the complex of strips and grazings. Therefore the houses of lord, freeman and peasant were contained within the nucleus of the village and from the village men went out daily to their work in the fields. The only exceptions were such habitations of ancient origin as the granges of the Cistercian abbeys which were set in the centre of their estates, and the solitary dwellings which survived the decay of a now deserted village. When the mass enclosure came in the years from 1750 to 1845, with a final tidying up under the General Enclosure Act of the latter date, it was a sensible step to move the farmstead from the village to the new consolidated holding, for there was no longer any reason for it to remain in the village. From Hampshire to Yorkshire, from West Suffolk to Shropshire, new Georgian, Regency or Victorian houses were built at the end of the new accommodation lanes or beside the roads between villages; and the barns and stables, bullock yards and wagon hovels were erected beside them so substantially as to be an embarrassment to later generations to whose new methods of grain storage, of stock management and of land cultivation they are peculiarly ill-suited. On a leisurely cross-country drive it is an instructive diversion to identify the ancient farmsteads and the new, and to build theories of settlement, enclosure and reconstruction. Quite often, a coherent and likely sequence of development emerges.

Britain—or rather, England—undertook voluntarily this re-distribution of its land at a date far earlier than integration began, imposed from above, in other Western European countries. In Germany, Holland, Switzerland, and in southern Italy, the process has only recently got under way. In such areas as the Eifel mountains between the Rhine and the Ardennes the Federal German Government was carrying out in 1961 the English eighteenth-century type of rural reconstruction, buying up all the scattered fields of the village holdings, creating new con-solidated farms each with its house and steading, and selling them back to such of the original owners as wanted them. As soon as the village houses were vacated commuters or week-enders moved in. In the Basel canton of Switzerland a very similar system of farm modernization was in progress at the same time. In Italy small farms of viable size were created in an ambi-tious but not successful programme in the 1950s, and the peasants from the hopelessly small holdings which were lost to them in the process were encouraged to move into urban employment. And the rationalization of Dutch land use has been in full spate ever since the end of the German Occupation in 1946. Here the Government has stood in the place of the squire or large farmers in the English enclosures, and having persuaded two-thirds of a community of land users to consent to integration it has re-shuffled the fragmented fields into forty- to eighty-acre farms, all equipped with house and buildings, and accommodated the displaced small farmers on land in the newly reclaimed polders of the Zuider Zee. In every case the repainting of the agrarian picture followed the example that had been set in England be-tween one and two hundred years before, except that the state took the initiative that, in England, had been at the hand of the private improver. The reasons for the delay in land rationalization of a century or more between Britain and the Continent will be examined later: briefly they were the early industrial development of the United Kingdom which stimulated a demand for food that could not be supplied by an agriculture still conducted in a near-mediaeval system of land distribution and use; and the high degree of protection against New World imports which Continental nations in general gave to their producers, thus cushioning them against the forces which in Britain made for the enlargement of holdings and the modernization of methods.

The teeming peasantry of Western Europe, which has survived into the present decade, grew more and more of an economic anachronism as the knowledge of, and materials for, agricultural improvement proliferated: but a picturesque and socially justifiable anachronism. Great numbers of people remained on the land in Europe when, in Britain, rural depopulation and the poverty of the labouring classes had come to the point at which half the countryside was living on public charity. The origins of the imbalance between the population and the opportunities for employment in the British countryside, which worried social reformers for nearly two hundred years, lay in these mid-eighteenth-century enclosures. The shape of rural society which existed until the 1920s was also drawn at this time. The gentry of all degrees had nearly a monopoly of the nation's wealth on, or under, their estates; and nonconformity and radicalism had hardly begun to challenge their social omnipotence. As often as not, they used their money to good purpose. Some went on the gaming tables, and much timber was clear-felled to pay gambling debts or for legitimate purposes like the education of Mrs Gaskell's Hamley children. But far more was spent on intelligent improvement; and here 'intelligent' is the operative word. Fielding and Addison and Johnson depicted many moneyed oafs; but in real life, from dukes down to minor gentry, from the Bedfords and Portlands down to the Lambtons of County Durham and the Assheton Smiths, were men who observed in their private lives the precept of Lord George Bentinck: 'The first ingredient in the happiness of a people is that the gentry should reside on their native soil, and spend their rents among those from whom they receive them.' The resident landowner administered the law, observed a tradition of prudent charity to the honest poor, assiduously jailed the delinquent or rebellious poor, read regularly in the journals of the new techniques of agriculture, and through the professional land agent whom he now employed tried them out himself and persuaded his larger tenants into agrarian experiment. Such men, and they abounded everywhere, were the father figures of the British countryside in the eighteenth century; and they continued, in peace and war, until the late nineteenth-century depression ended both rural prosperity and this admirable tradition of benevolent paternalism. At Hagley Hall the morning prayers always included the supplication, 'teach us to be just to those dependent on us'!

The squire, peer or commoner, ruled the countryside with an autocracy that was usually well-intentioned but was often detached from reality. The daily life of the village had, from the late seventeenth century, come to be controlled to a great extent by the principal farmers and tradesmen in vestry assembled, and it was through them and their elected officers—the church-wardens, overseer, surveyor and constable—that the poor laws were administered, the dole of public charity spread thinly, the roads (except for the new turnpikes) grudgingly repaired, local nuisances abated, the church decently maintained, and the bastard and the infirm and the aged kept slightly on the right side of starvation. During the nineteenth century the parish vestry, which was often a self-cooptative and hereditary bureaucracy, had its powers and its duties whittled away by the new public authorities. From county councils down to boards of guardians; but for two centuries these farmers and tradesmen in vestry assembled were the noncommissioned officers of the village, owing obedience only to the gentry gathered on the bench at quarter sessions. They replaced the mediaeval chain of authority from the lord of the manor through his steward to the manorial courts and the bailiffs and reeves who were the lowest leaders of local society; and they were the ancestors of the county, rural and parish councils who now wield authority. Each little cell of local society virtually ruled itself through its own most solid members. It was this high degree of self-autonomy that gave the squire and his larger tenants and the substantial freeholders the robust attitudes that Fielding portrayed in Squire Western and Hardy depicted in his petty tyrants of Wessex.

The poverty and abject dependence of the hired labourers of the eighteenth century had a somewhat less picturesque aspect. They were a class of landless men, unique in Europe at that time, who had been displaced from their small plots of land and their common rights by the final phases of enclosure. On the whole, contemporary society approved the change in their condition. It had seen the commons as 'seminaries of a lazy, thieving sort of people', and the occupiers of the last relics of the little mediaeval holdings as 'a set of very miserable men. They fare extremely hard, work without intermission like a horse, and practise every lesson of diligence and frugality, without being able to soften their present lot.' In a period of improving agriculture there was some economic justification for this view. Without capital, the small man could not buy the implements for proper cultivation, or improve the equipment and the condition of his land, or procure good seed, or stock well enough, or experiment. A nation on the threshold of an industrial revolution could properly regard him as a non-runner in the national economy. One author of the Board of Agriculture's county surveys at the end of the eighteenth century called him a peasant; and went on to describe the master of one of the recently enclosed farms as a professional farmer. There was a wealth of social and economic truth in the distinction. A nation of peasants could never feed a nation of factory workers.

Unhappily, when these landless men were without work, they were completely without the means of subsistence, except for what they could grow in their cottage gardens or rear in their cottage pigstyes. The rural employers, from farmers to tradesmen and journeymen, employed them at starvation wages; and the Poor Law system, under parochial control, supplemented these wages to the point where a bare existence became just possible. An Act of 1722 permitted the foundation of parish workhouses, and to these many decent men and women were driven to pauperdom. Many of them emerged only to be tumbled into the parish shell, jogged to the churchyard in the parish cart, and there, cheaply shrouded, thrust into the cold earth. This was the penalty of agricultural progress. This rural poverty, with generation after generation born to hopelessness, remained in diminishing degree into the twentieth century; and many elderly men still at work today were reared in homes to which their fathers brought back only their twelve shillings a week. The whole family, at the earliest possible age, had to set out to supplement this tiny income. The smallest children went birdscaring through the hours of daylight, with a raw turnip for sustenance. The women, huddled into layers of old rags, spudded thistles or planted potatoes. And everyone, in leisure minutes, busied themselves in such cottage industries as straw-plaiting or lace-making. But this source of income, too, was doomed; and it disappeared altogether when the old cottage industries were absorbed into the new factories.

The poverty of the landless day-labourers came to one peak when food prices soared during the Napoleonic Wars and wages stood nearly still at seven shillings a week. It came to a second, intolerable peak, in 1816, when the wars were over, the harvest season was wet and the inevitable period of post-war depression set in. Then 'Bread or Blood' gangs of starving men terrorized East Anglia. It came to a third and final peak, the awful grand climacteric of pauper rebellion in Britain, in 1830. Landless labourers who did not emigrate in desperation joined the Captain Swing mobs of hopeless countrymen. These gangs smashed the new threshing machines for the reason that they were depriving them of their winter work with a flail in the barn, and burnt ricks for no reason at all except in unreasoning protest against economic forces which were, perhaps, beyond the control of anyone. Their fellow countrymen of more substance often recognized the justice of their cause. Many a farmer joined them, or met the demands of his men as far as he was able, or prompted them to press the parson to abate the tithes he paid so that he could afford to pay better wages. A frightened government, with the French Revolution fresh in mind, set up special commissions of assize which hanged nine men and boys, transported 457, and imprisoned 400. There were no more risings, and the agricultural labourer went back to work at seven shillings a week, if he was fortunate enough to have work to go to.

Enclosure was undoubtedly one cause of this pitiful situation; but the fundamental reason was the conjunction of enclosure in England with the large increase in population which was taking place throughout Western Europe, caused by a lowering of the age of marriage and a reduction in the mortality rate. Quite early in the eighteenth century some shrewd observers became anxious at the trend in population, and forecast famine. In 1650 there had probably been a 100 million people in the whole of Europe, in 1750 there were 140 million; in 1850, 266 million. The increase occurred at a time when in many countries, and in Britain in particular, the network of farms was becoming fixed in a pattern which remained little changed until the Second Great War. The opportunities for entry into farming were therefore restricted largely to the natural casualty rate among tenants and owner-occupiers through death, retirement or bankruptcy. Reclamation had virtually reached its limit in all but the abnormal circumstances of war-time boom in prices; and the sub-division of peasant holdings to give land to younger sons was now rarely possible because—in England at any rate—there were almost no peasant holdings left to divide. The rural economy had become inelastic. It could be stretched no further to accommodate the hundreds of thousands of new country children asking to be fed and young men seeking to be employed. The natural outlets were the towns and the colonies, but the rate of movement out of rural areas failed to keep pace with the increase in rural population. It was not until the 1940s that equilibrium, lost early in the eighteenth century, was regained and the number of farm jobs and the number of farm workers to do them came into balance again. Ironically, the sentimentalists thereupon began to deplore the 'drift from the land'—but this is jumping too far ahead.

The situation on the Continent was different. The same increase in population was occurring, but the pattern of land tenure had changed relatively little as compared with the revolution in the social structure of rural Britain, and the surplus people were mainly absorbed within the peasant society. In England and Scotland in particular, a family with no land or paid employment was a family with nothing, except charity, on which to live. In France and Germany and Switzerland there were comparatively few country people with no holding of land whatever, however small it may have become through sub-division. With some land one could keep starvation at arm's length, if not out of sight: a cow, a cabbage patch, a half-acre of grain stood between a family and death. To this extent, the peasants of Western Europe might be poor indeed; but they never plumbed the depths of the despair in which the English day labourer's family lived for generation after generation. To be sure there were some landless men in Europe. In lowland Switzerland at the beginning of the eighteenth century one family in five was without arable land, but probably enjoyed grazing rights. In Holland the eighteenth-century distribution of rural population among landed and landless categories showed between one family in four or five to be without landed resources. For comparison, an estimate for England in 1700 was that there were 573,000 day-labourers and 330,000 farmers; or nearly two families out of three were landless. And in 1831 there were 686,000 English day-labourers and 275,100 farmers; or nearly three families out of four landless. The figures may need to be treated with caution; but even so, the disparity is evident enough.

The difference went deeper than this. In France on the eve of the Revolution one-third of the land was either owned or cheaply rented by peasants; and in some areas sixty per cent was farmed by peasants and only forty per cent by larger farmers. True, many of the small holdings were very small indeed. Van Bath gives typical figures: in Limousin over half the peasant holdings were of less than four acres, and in Loiret over three-quarters were smaller than nine acres. But in England, three-quarters of the rural families had no land at all. The difference was attributable to many things; but mostly to the fact that the French seigneur was content—often anxious—to remain a rentier, and was not interested in taking his estate in hand and improving it. Such enclosure as there was tended to be in favour of the peasantry, not to his disadvantage. For this reason French agriculture stood comparatively still at a time when British farming was progressing; but the national economy did not suffer, as

Britain's would have done in these circumstances, because in France there were few industrial and agriculturally unproductive mouths to be fed. The great part of the French nation remained within a subsistence economy. Though the situation in the north German states more closely resembled that in England, with Prussia in particular becoming a country of big landowning farmers, the south German states remained in a largely peasant agriculture.

These differences in the stratification of rural society in England and Western Europe, which became firmly drawn in the eighteenth century, were accentuated in the next hundred years by the divergence in the policies pursued by governments. The nations with self-subsistent peasantries preserved them by protective tariffs against New World production. The countries with highly developed systems of large farms permitted the free trade winds to blow coldly upon their agricultures. The results of these policies over peasantry and protection had a fundamental bearing upon affairs right up to the time when the European Economic Community was founded by the Treaty of Rome in 1957.

CHAPTER SEVEN

Nineteenth-Century Revolution

Rural Britain in the year 1800 was unique in Western Europe not merely for the landless poverty of its labouring class but for the whole edifice of its society. Richard Rush, the American ambassador, explained the reason when he wrote a few years later of the upper classes: 'They have houses in London . . . but their homes are in the country. This spreads the ambition among other classes, and the taste for rural life, however diversified or graduated the scale, becomes widely diffused.' The enjoyment of the countryside became a profession among those who were most deeply committed to their estates; and one of the elements of their enduring pleasure was a thriving and tidy tenantry. In such a situation any considerable echo of the French Revolution in Britain became impossible, although starvation sat on the threshold of every other cottage; for the patriarchy of the landed classes was a benevolent one within the context of this vigorous age, and there was a rough-and-ready egalitarianism which enabled the hat-touching yeoman and the royal duke to meet and eat as equals at the Woburn and the Holkham Sheep Shearings. Both drank equally hard, a habit acquired at school; both bet, within or beyond their means, on Tom Cribb and cheered at the ringside together; to both the foxhunt was the highlight of the winter week, whether as the invited guest of the owner of the private pack or a member of the new subscription pack; in the heart of both, rural England was the only England, and almost all England was rural. In 1809 Miss Berry walked one June day with her father and her sister to the fields between Paddington and Bayswater . . . 'we sat for some time on the cocks of hay, which I really enjoyed'; the Old Berkeley hounds drew the coverts in Kensington Gardens; and a stag was run up to the door-ways of the new houses in Russell Square.

Only in shooting did the pursuits of all rural classes diverge, for the laws preserved game to large landlords and a few privileged exceptions among other people and denied it to most farmers. This discrimination bred the poaching gangs which terrorized the countryside with the sympathy, if not the active support, of the tenant farmers whose enclosure hedges had to be left untrimmed for game coverts, although many acres of land for which they paid rent were thereby made unproductive by the spread of foliage. Such matters excepted, the landlord from duke to minor squire and the farmer down to the smallest tenant shared the same interests in working hours as in leisure hours. Such circumstances bred good neighbourliness, set the scene for co-operation in agricultural progress, and kept the guillotine beyond the Straits of Dover. The English country gentlemen have been condemned for many sins of commission and omission; but if it had not been that 'their homes are in the country' English farming would have remained unproductive and unimproved.

For this was the Age of Improvement; and it was also the Age of Agricultural Journalism, the first great flowering of the art of technical reporting. Indeed it may be that without the journalism the science and practice of improvement in farming would have gone unnoticed or perhaps scarcely existed. Like justice, progress in agriculture had both to be practised and to be seen to be practised; for without the written report only local advances could be made, and those slowly and wastefully. Without Coke and Bakewell, William Marshall and Arthur Young could not have written as significantly as they did; and without Marshall and Young, Thomas Coke and Robert Bakewell would have seen their work remain only locally significant. Every Johnson needs his Boswell; and the late eighteenth-century and early nineteenth-century Johnsons of agriculture—men every bit as intent and pontifical as the doctor—were magnificently served by their reporters.

Of the two, Marshall and Young, William Marshall was the sounder, and the duller, and therefore received less popular acclaim in his own day and less honour at the hands of historians. He was colourless, heavy, schematic; an assiduous analyst of systems and techniques, his assessments were shrewd and just;

and he was himself a successful farmer. It was he who first proposed that a Board of Agriculture should be set up, with its
primary object the surveying of the agricultural practices and the
rural economies of England and Wales. He lost the idea, and
the credit, to others; and became an embittered man. But he
pursued the scheme of the surveys himself and in the twelve
years from 1787 to 1798 he published twelve volumes of description and critical analysis, in great depth, of English and Welsh
farming in the broadest sense. As far as they can be judged at a
distance of more than a century and a half, his *Rural Oeconomies*
are models of accurate reporting and consistent and considered
judgments: turgid and tedious, but vast repositories of reliable
facts. Late in his life (1745-1818) he dissected the reports of the
new Board of Agriculture's surveyors, in which his successful
rival Arthur Young took a leading part, and exposed many of
them as the specious products of agricultural theorists, written
at a distance from their subject-matter both in space and thought.
He died a disappointed man, but he left a legacy of material
that is vital to an understanding of the farming of his time.

Young was his rival in the sense that both men sought to
attract the attention of their contemporaries by the skill of their
reporting and so to win adherents to their respective doctrines
of agricultural progress; and Young was successful in that he
had most of the tricks of the trade tucked up his sleeve. Marshall
had a clear mind and an honest pen, no more. These make a
sound reporter, never a brilliant one. Young was brilliant, but
often unsound. In his early life he moved from failure to failure
—as a clerk, a littérateur, a farmer. But like other gifted and
erratic men, his accumulated experiences linked together in the
course of time into a completed jigsaw picture that portrayed a
racy, stylish, observant author who was more than a mere technical reporter. The total effect of his knowledge, his observation
and his wit made him an agricultural journalist whose only peers
have been James Caird of *The Times*, Rider Haggard and A. G.
Street.

Born in 1741, Young began to pour out his farming books in
1768, starting with regional surveys of the south, north, and east
of England, of Ireland and of France. In 1784 he published the

first of his monthly *Annals of Agriculture*, the forty-six volumes of which were farming magazines of a very high calibre. In 1794, as first secretary of Pitt's new Board of Agriculture, he superintended the preparation of the Board's county farming surveys, of which he himself wrote six; and although these were of uneven merit they still remain unchallenged as the only detailed description of the agriculture of the whole of England and Wales, from the husbandries of arable and stock farms through local finance and forestry to rural sociology. He died in 1820—blind, melancholic, poor, as sad a failure in his family life as he had ever been in any of his ventures as a youth, but a man with whom every landlord and farmer of note in Britain was proud to claim acquaintance. No countryman could hope for a better epitaph. The two men, the dull but reliable Marshall and the gay but unreliable Young, complemented each other exactly, so that through their eyes and pens the farming of the turn of the eighteenth and nineteenth centuries comes alive. It is for this reason that it is not easy to say how much in the agriculture of the time was innovation and progress, and how much was neither, but was merely being noted down for posterity for the first time.

It is usual to give the Improver most of the benefit of the doubt. Often this is being over-generous. This is especially the case with the man who, above all others, was father-figure of his age and calling, Robert Bakewell. That judgment is only less than fair if it is as creditable to be a publicist of talent as it is to be a livestock breeder of genius. Bakewell possessed in a high degree the arts of plagiarism and propaganda: he plagiarized the little-known work of clever breeders, and propagated his own image as a livestock improver with consummate skill. But, by the combination, he also promoted among his contemporaries a concept of stock selection and line breeding which was very necessary if a faster and wider amelioration of farm stock was to be achieved; and he pinpointed in his own person, for later generations of livestock husbandmen and agricultural historians, the particular achievement of his age. Nearly every period throws up such a man: a Morris, to borrow the art of another nation and use his idiosyncracies to give it a vogue; a Wells, to fasten

upon some facts of science and elaborate them with his imagination; a Boutflour, to see the patent faults of the old-fashioned
cow-keeper and serve his generation well by castigating them.
Bakewell stood at the top of this line of descent. The son of a
yeoman farmer of Dishley Grange, Loughborough, he developed
an interest in and a talent for livestock breeding, which he seems
to have first exercised about 1745 when he was a youth of twenty.
Arthur Young, who was Bakewell's most loyal, vocal and uncritical publicist, claimed that the young man had 'perfectly new'
ideas of how to improve stock, and acclaimed him the pioneer
of the new methods. William Marshall, sounder and more critical
as he always was, made it clear that Bakewell borrowed his
system of in-breeding from some of the great racehorse owners;
that as a cattle improver he built upon a solid foundation already
laid down by quieter, humbler men; and that even in Bakewell's
heyday his cattle and sheep were not the best, but merely the
best publicized.

None the less, Robert Bakewell deserves well of history if only
for one achievement: he concentrated public attention upon the
prime need of the day, the production of animals which would
grow more meat faster, in order that the rising demand for food
by the steadily increasing population could be met. His objective
in cattle was the breeding of a 'beast which will weigh most in
the most valuable joints, not fifty stone divided into thirty stone
in coarse boiling and twenty stone in roasting pieces, but vice
versa'. He took the best Longhorn stock he could find, from
Webster of Canley, mated like to like, and brought in some out-
crosses which possessed the characteristics lacking in his main
lines of breeding stock. In the end he produced from the old
useful dual-purpose animal a new single-purpose beef beast in
which the propensity to produce milk had been lost, which was
of little importance where other dairy breeds were available; and
from which prolificacy had nearly disappeared, which was a
lethal defect. In the result, Bakewell's line of Longhorn cattle
virtually died out within a few decades. If it had not been that
he had bred a mortal factor into his stock—the inability to perpetuate themselves—and for the gullibility of too many farmers
in being persuaded by the publicists that the only good Long-

horn was a Dishley Longhorn, this old and good breed could well have dominated the cattle husbandry of the nineteenth century as it had that of the eighteenth.

The 'Wizard of Dishley', as his propagandists called him, also set out to 'improve' sheep by breeding into them the faculties of more rapid growth and greater weight. Here again Bakewell was correct in his analysis of the economic situation: mutton would be demanded in greater quantities, and the man who could grow it the most efficiently would profit. So he took the ancient midland longwool sheep, both the Leicester and to some extent its cousin the Lincoln, and by selective mating, the ruthless culling of the slower growers, and an extensive progeny testing system worked by letting his sires out to hire so that they could be widely assessed, he produced the New or Dishley Leicester. In the result, here again, he had bred out most of the wool; but more important, he also produced and fixed a strain which had become excessively fat in the less valuable joints; and, once again, he lost both prolificacy and milk. A contemporary described the breed, with polysyllabic insight: 'its excessive tendency to obesity abates the procreative and lactiferous powers.' The coarseness and fatness of the mutton of the New Leicester have never been remedied: the few pure Leicesters which still survive possess the faults in full measure. But, in time, fecundity was bred back into it; and the result was something that Bakewell had neither intended nor imagined, as far as the workings of his secretive mind can now be judged—he guarded his failures closely from the inquisitive, but employed all the tricks of showmanship to publicize his successes. This unexpected result was the production, in time, of a breed of crossing rams which virtually altered the appearance and the performance of half the sheep in the Old World and the New.

The process may best be explained by skipping a century and a half and looking at the British method of fat lamb production, which is the most effective in the world. It is based on combining the desirable characteristics of three different types of sheep. First, the breeder takes a ram of a breed in which the characteristic of prolificacy has been fixed, usually the Border Leicester. He mates this to an upland ewe which has outstanding maternal qualities, and in particular a heavy milk yield, usually the Cheviot. The hybrid ewe lamb of this Border Leicester × Cheviot mating the breeder sells to a Lowland flockmaster, who in turn mates the ewe to a ram of a breed in which a high quality of carcase has been fixed, often a Suffolk. In the final result the lambs of this Suffolk × Border Leicester-Cheviot ancestry are numerous, from the inherited prolificacy of the Border Leicester; they grow fast, from the inherited heavy milk yield of their dams; and they are of the most profitable conformation and they 'finish' well—that is, they put on sufficient fat at the right age to give a carcase of the desired lean-fat proportions—from the inherited meat qualities of their Down sire. This chain of breeding does not necessarily give the best carcase, or the fastest growth, or the most lambs: in each of these characters the Down × Half-Bred cross is equalled, or excelled, by other breeds; but no other breed possesses all three in such a high degree. The same process of hybridization is applied to other species; in cattle, by the Blue-Grey breeders of the Scottish Borders; in pigs, by New Zealand geneticists and by commercial pig-meat companies in Britain. But it is in sheep that it has its greatest use, and its greatest effect.

It was by providing one of the bases of this Down × Half-Bred lamb that Robert Bakewell made his greatest contribution to livestock husbandry. He certainly never had the breeding of a prolific crossing ram in mind when he evolved the New Leicester; and it was only slowly and tortuously that men who bought his stock bred back into it the fecundity which it had lost in Bakewell's hands. The first Dishley Leicesters emerged in about 1770; the new breed reached the height of its fame in 1789, when Bakewell hired three of his rams for a season for twelve hundred guineas, and received three thousand guineas from his whole letting of Dishley tups. It was nearly twenty years before the Border sheepmasters who had taken his stock north—notably the brothers Culley—were able to complete the elimination of unprolificacy by ruthless culling, and to turn their Border Leicesters into the fecund, thrifty and efficient sheep that they remain to this day.

George Culley has never had the recognition that is his due:

he lacked the publicists and the showmanship that set a somewhat spurious seal upon Bakewell's fame. Therefore he has had
to be judged on his own writings, which were sensible and
modest; and on the visible result of his life's work, the Border
Leicester breed, which is a fine monument to any man. He himself was a fairly uncritical disciple of Bakewell, whose breeding
methods he emulated, as far as they could be discovered. In this
discipleship he was joined by livestock breeders who, in the
closing years of the eighteenth century and the first half of the
nineteenth, took the regional types of British sheep and cattle,
selected the required traits, and by in-breeding built into them
some degree of homozygosity. Their names, if not legion, make
up a long roll-call of agricultural fame: Ellman with the Southdown fixed from an old sheep of the chalk hills of the south-east,
David Dunn and the Blackfaces which moved north from the
Pennines to populate most of Scotland's sheep walks; Robson
who concentrated into the mediaeval monastic hill sheep of the
Cheviot hills the best maternal characters of any breed in Britain.
In cattle, Tomkins evolved the Hereford breed from closely-
related varieties of white-faced red and grey stock of the Welsh
Borders; and Davey in Devon turned the ancient working beast
of the West Country into a beef animal of high meat quality.

These tunes, it will be observed, were all played upon British
notes. The Improvers took the best they could find in existing
types of stock and compressed them into moulds from which
efficient replicas could be produced for ever after. In this imported blood played some part, indirectly. Bakewell's Longhorn,
Tomkins's Hereford, the white-faced and finch-backed cattle of
Gloucestershire, were all probably bred from stock into which
there had been some introduction of Low Countries blood. Only
in Scotland were the old indigenous breeds which were making
up into the great Scottish beef of yesterday proceeding by
internal and wholly native selection.

The debt which British livestock breeders owe to their fellows
in the Low Countries is usually acknowledged only in respect of
the modern Friesian cow; and a far older and not less significant
borrowing is rarely recognized and even more rarely given due
weight. In the same way, the revolution which was wrought in

the livestock of Western Europe and Scandinavia in the nineteenth century by the wisespread use of improved British breeds is largely ignored, and in many instances now forgotten. The repercussions of the explosive genetics of Bakewell, Ellman and Webb, Culley, the Collings, Bates and the Booths in Britain were, indeed, felt not only through the Continent but also through the world.

The movement was a two-way one. First, there had to flow into England the raw material for processing. This was principally the north-west European type of cattle of which the black-and-white British Friesian is the modern representative. The Continental origins of this widespread variety are undocumented, but it appears to have originated in what is now north-west Germany, and thence spread out into a circle the perimeter of which runs through Russia, Georgia, Italy, France and Eire. In the eighteenth century it took its most important step, the replenishing of the Dutch grazings which had been emptied by rinderpest of their local strain of red and white cattle. The interbreeding which then took place between the black-and-white and the stronger built red-and-white (now the M.Y.R. dual-purpose breed) resulted in an improvement of the invading, black-and-whites in hardiness, body size and propensity to flesh, leaving the high milking qualities of the black-and-white unharmed. As this was happening, or even a century before, English improvers whose very names have been lost to history brought some of this red-and-white and black-and-white stock into both Kent and Lincolnshire. Agricultural writers around the end of the seventeenth century were describing it as the pied, Dutch, or Holderness breed of Lincolnshire: 'very bulky', 'heavy milking', 'require great Attendance and the best of Food', and 'Dutch-ars'd' (from the great span of the hip-bones) were the contemporary descriptions. The red-and-whites appear to have been recognized as the more valuable. In course of time, and by much cross-breeding with the existing British red types, a regional type was evolved in an area which stretched from Norfolk to Durham. These hybrid cattle, with their high production of milk, large size and rapid fleshing, were obvious victims for the improvers' attention. The word 'victim' is used because, over the decades and centuries, breeders managed to lose either milk yield, or fleshing quality and size; so that in the end they left the livestock husbandman with animals which could compete neither with the best of the dairy cows nor the best of the beef breeds. That, however, lay in the future.

In the early eighteenth century the disciples of Bakewell applied his methods of in-breeding to several types of cattle which had developed from these European imports. The most famous of the improvers were the Colling brothers in the Darlington area of Yorkshire, Thomas Booth of Studley, and Thomas Bates of Kirklevington. These men initiated a fashion for 'pedigree' breeding such as their master, Robert Bakewell, had never engendered; the fashion became a mania; and in the process improvers in Europe became infected. It would be idle to deny that the worst excesses of breeders still fumbling in the dawn of the science of genetics did considerable harm to much useful stock; and it would be foolish to assert that no good emerged from their activities. On balance, there was certainly far more good than harm; but the peak of perfection in cattle did not issue from the improvers' hands, as has often been asserted. The Shorthorn, which dominated British cattle from the war of Napoleon to the war of Hitler, is a case in point. The type had been manufactured mainly over the eighteenth century, from Dutch and British blood with a probable addition of Normandy blood; and it was the dominant dual-purpose breed in north-eastern England. It had, for the time, a very large milk yield of five to six gallons at the peak of lactation; and it grew, in time, to a very great weight—figures are quoted of 22cwt at five years old—with a readiness in some strains to fatten as three-year-olds at 15cwt. These performances, it should be noted, would be acceptable today—particularly on a cheap diet the equivalent of the low-protein, high-fibre rations of the late eighteenth century. But the type failed in two particulars. The lactation curve rose high, but was not level: that meant that the milk yield climbed rapidly to a peak six weeks or so after calving and fell off again rapidly. This, at that time, was not important. Little milk was drunk, most was manufactured into cheese; and there was little disadvantage and much merit in having a flush of spring and summer milk and a dry cow in the difficult feeding months of winter. Only as liquid milk consumption grew—and this, in any case, was mainly provided for by the town dairies—was it necessary to have a level production through the year.

The second failure lay in the conformation of the eighteenth-century Shorthorn. This still carried, as a legacy of the draught oxen days which were not yet over, a great weight of muscular lean meat around the shoulders and a relatively light rear end, where the choicer cuts lay. Here again, this was not as great a fault as some agricultural historians have made it out to be. Perfectly acceptable steaks could be cut out of the shoulders; the central rib cuts were sound; and only the fashionable tables where a great weight of rear cut was expected were badly served. The first approach by the improvers to this crude but highly efficient converter of food into a coarse and livery beef and a milk of somewhat low quality was to isolate what appeared to them to be a thrifty feeder of medium size, small bone and well-coloured, fine-grained lean meat; to ignore milking propensities entirely; and, by Bakewellian line breeding carried to the extreme limit of genetic safety (and sometimes beyond), to fix the type into a true-breeding strain. The father-figures of this Shorthorn breed were the Collings brothers, Althorpe and Vane Tempest, the Booths and—in Scotland—Barclay, Hay and Cruickshank. They succeeded in producing a beef beast that was efficient in every sense of the word except one: it was a poor converter of food into meat. It had also, of course, virtually ceased to milk, so much so that it was often unable to suckle its calf, which had to be put on to a nurse cow.

It was not until the 1830s that the Shorthorn had milk bred back into it by Thomas Bates. 'The dairy has been disregarded', wrote the agricultural commentator of this decade, Youatt; and even the highly prejudiced breed historian Wright admitted that 'it is notorious that many of the most superior Shorthorns do not possess milking quality in an eminent degree'. The milk that Bates restored to the breed was far less than it had once possessed; and until late in the nineteenth century its critics wrote pungently of its shortcomings. A leading dairyman of that leading dairy county, Cheshire, was heard to remark at the Royal

Show of 1864 that if he wanted milk he would prefer that his cows should be matched to the son of his neighbour's best milking cow than to a bull of Bates's; and The Druid himself, whose fluent and lively pen divided itself between sport and farming, said that any allusion to good milking pedigree in a sale catalogue of Shorthorns was regarded as an apology for doubtful blood, such was the disregard of the ordinary run of pedigree Shorthorn breeders for the milch quality of their stock.

From the superior vantage point of a century's hindsight it is easy to condemn these improvers for their sins of omission. They had taken up the tools of in-breeding, line-breeding and selective crossing which had been brought to their attention by Robert Bakewell; and they used them to shape the raw material of their occupation into patterns either utilitarian or fancy. The fancy patterns devised by those into whose blood the mania of pedigree showing had entered were a gross abuse of the useful livestock which they ruined. The utilitarians had a better excuse: they wrought to what they saw as a good end. Often it was. There was room, indeed there was need, in the early nineteenth century for specialized beef beasts, both in the Old World and in the New. And, by and large, the types they produced served the purpose as well as any could hope to do either then or for a century afterwards. Often, indeed, good intention was ruined by commercial short-sightedness or careless use of the powerful instrument of in-breeding; and this was particularly so in the loss of milking quality. But it would have required a prophet to forecast that in a few decades the network of railways which was to cover Britain would open up the liquid milk markets of the towns to livestock farmers who lived a hundred or two hundred miles away; although as early as 1849 it was noted that the profitability of land for many miles around Liverpool had 'somewhat diminished because of the abundant supply of milk' that was beginning to come in by rail from further afield. And it is, perhaps, no exaggeration to say that no breeder at this time was skilful enough to breed for more than one attribute at a time; so that it was nearly inevitable that if one bred for beef conformation in cattle one must lose milk yield, and if one bred for rapid fleshing in sheep one lost prolificacy. Selection for more than one factor in livestock breeding is still an art—or a science —that still eludes all but the most skilful, or those with most luck. All in all, the profit and loss account of the livestock improvers in the century from 1750 to 1850—and even beyond— showed a credit balance; but not as large a one as has often been claimed.

Their achievements were sufficiently spectacular, if not always sufficiently sound, to attract the attention of stockmen overseas. This again came about through a combination of the intrinsic merit of the new stock and the wide publicity given to them by the agricultural authors and journalists who proliferated in the early years of the nineteenth century. Here again it is impossible to say whether the product was so good that the salesmanship was nearly irrelevant, or the salesmanship was so effective that it could have sold anything. If any of Bakewell's Longhorns went to the Continent, trace of their export is now lost; and there is certainly no evidence of Longhorn cross to be seen now in the main European breeds. Perhaps the significance of the British livestock revolution had not crossed the Channel until the Longhorn had entered upon its decline. Of Shorthorn crosses on French stock in particular there is ample testimony. As early as 1810 a white Shorthorn bull was put upon the white stock of the village of Charole, and this sire certainly played some part in the development of the now great and international beef breed of Charolais cattle. From the third or fourth decade of the nineteenth century Shorthorns of dual-purpose type were also crossed on the varieties of Pie Rouge cattle, and this crossing has continued into recent years. In Scotland, the dairy breed of Ayrshire was manufactured in the south-western counties in the closing decades of the eighteenth century, from Dutch and Channel Island crosses upon a northern Longhorn cow; and this had such obvious merit in hardiness, thriftiness and its heavy yield of milk even on poor keep that the pure breed was established in Scandinavia, where it has since developed on distinctive but not dissimilar lines from its Scottish cousins.

The influence of the new English stock upon European breeds was more marked in sheep, however, than it was in cattle; and there are few types of sheep in northern and central France, western Germany and Holland that are not descended from New or Border Leicester or Southdown stock shipped over in the early and middle nineteenth century. Some of these carry the visible marks of this remote parentage to this day: the Texel of Holland is patently of Border Leicester descent, and the highly prolific Bleu de Maine breed has developed on parallel lines to the Blue or Hexham Leicester of the English–Scottish Border, even to the distinctive face colouring. Many of the French Merino hybrids were developed from Southdown crosses upon the Rambouillet Merino. The Île de France, largely used for the production of early winter lambs in the sheephouses of the Paris region, is a notable example. And the Southdown itself was imported into France and naturalized there early enough for most of the French stock still to carry the dark tinge to the face which disappeared from the English Southdown over half a century ago. So fundamental has been the influence of these two types in particular—the varieties of Leicester and the Southdown —upon Western European sheep that it is possible to walk through a Continental livestock show, the Paris International Salon, for instance—and see scarcely a fat-lamb producing breed exhibited that is not obviously partly of British origin.

In other spheres of farming, British influence on European materials and techniques was negligible. Rather the reverse, for great areas of British agricultural practice, in the precise sense of 'agricultural', were founded upon Continental borrowings. It has been seen that these had been frequent from the sixteenth century onwards; and, indeed, the whole basis of British farming was Continental in the sense that it was imported, partly made, by the Saxon settlers and had been refreshed by new importations of ideas, and some materials, since then. In the eighteenth century, English arable husbandry in particular was stimulated and improved by the slow infiltration of European practices. The wellhead was the intensively cultivated areas of Flanders and Brabant, where the English innovators went frequently to drink of the agrarian wisdom distilled by the agrarian craftsmen whose husbandry had been so concentrated by the pressure of population over several centuries that their techniques

in the arable and grass fields were closer to market garden cropping than conventional, extensive farming. In the adjoining
French province of Artois, and up the length of the Rhine valley
from Westphalia to Bavaria and westwards into Alsace the arable
husbandry was of a scarcely lower order. England was, in many
ways, until the eighteenth century an agricultural backwater in
which efficient practices of cereal, root, grass and industrial
cropping were slow to develop. The beginnings of illumination
came when Weston reported back to Restoration England the
Flemish development of fodder cropping; as the means of mass
communication developed, knowledge slowly spread through the
upper crust of British farming gentry. The first important British
improvement followed upon Weston's analysis of the typical
Flemish rotation: flax with a catchcrop of turnips following, and
then a cereal with clover undersown to stand as a grazing crop
for some seasons. In England this developed into a more intensive arable rotation of five courses with a wheat and turnip
catchcrop, and then potatoes replacing the second and third
clover years. This shift, by a remarkable exercise in empiricism,
was nearly self-manuring, for the grazing crops of turnips and
clover built up fertility for the succeeding main cash crops of
oats, wheat and potatoes. The shift was very close to the later,
and far better known, Norfolk four-course for which the credit
has been put at the doors of 'Turnip' Townshend and Coke of
Norfolk. These were worthy and estimable English landlords
who stood in mixed farming in the same relationship to the great
publicists Marshall and Young as Bakewell stood in livestock
improvement. They, like Bakewell, were less inventors than
exemplars—but, of course, scarcely the less useful for that.

As long ago as the 1880s, the German economic historians
Backhaus and Böhure illustrated from the manorial account
books the progressive diminution of the proportion of fallow in
the arable acreage that such rationalized cropping methods had
brought about even on estates as far from the Flanders–Brabant
hub as the Harz and Saxony. On average nearly forty per cent of
the land had been fallowed in the early years of the eighteenth
century; by 1850 three of the estates had no fallow at all, one had
less than one per cent, and the fifth had 2·8 per cent. There were

many incidental reasons for this dramatic change—one estate was kept partly uncropped for hunting in the earlier period—but the major reasons were the development of cleaning crops which took the place of the fallow, and the higher proportion of fodder crops in the rotations which enabled more livestock to be kept, increased the amount of manure available, and made unnecessary the natural regeneration of fertility which occurs in land un-cropped for a period.

The limitations which shortage of manure imposed on crop production are not easy to appreciate today, when nearly all fertilizer comes in bags from the chemical manufacturers and animal manure is a nuisance which costs money to dispose of. The most highly cropped areas in the eighteenth and nineteenth centuries had to rely on two sources for their crop nutrients: the livestock which fed upon the fodder crops grown in the rotation —either eating the turnips in the fields and dunging there as well, or being fed roots in the stalls whence the dung was carted out into the fields—and the extraneous manures. Van Bath lists many of the materials which the husbandmen of Flanders applied to their arable land: city refuse and street sweepings, pigeons' dung, wood ash, the excrement from the town privies, rotted turf and the oil cakes that were the residues from the processing of oil seed crops. The first 'artificial fertilizers' were also appear-ing; but this was an English development rather than a Con-tinental one.

It was the European progress in cereal, root, fodder and in-dustrial crops of the arable field that was the overwhelmingly important contribution of the Old World to agriculture—again in the precise sense—in this period. Perhaps in the oldest cereal crops of the temperate regions British farmers held a technical advantage; this will be discussed shortly. The newest cereal, maize, played no significant part in British farming until the mid-twentieth-century crop breeders bred varieties which were able to grow and ripen in the short British summer; but on the Continent it spread north from Spain and Portugal into central Europe, where it became an important deep-rooted cleaning crop in the rotation, with a yield three times greater than that of wheat and providing good food for man, beast and bird. The supremely productive food crop, the potato, was slow to gain recognition. It entered into Old World written history in a reference in 1536 when a Spanish expedition penetrated the interior of Colombia which, with Peru and Bolivia, was its native home; and it was certainly being eaten, but not necessarily cultivated, at Seville in 1573. A quarter of a century later Gerard in his *Herbal* fathered the myth that this root came from Virginia; and it was an easy transition to the equally false belief that one of the great English pirates—either Raleigh or Drake was named —brought it to Europe. A century and a half was to pass before the potato was cultivated on any scale in Britain, and then only as a cheap food in a time of high cereal prices. It gained a firm foothold in France and Holland and Germany not very much earlier, as a break crop in the cereal rotation; and in this it served a most useful purpose because the deep cultivation that was necessary cleaned the ground thoroughly and the heavy manuring left the right residue of fertility for a succeeding cereal crop. This has remained its position in the farming cycle ever since, except that in the great potato-growing areas cereals are treated rather as the break crops between the potato years.

Perhaps in all Western Europe the supreme expertise in the cultivation of the potato was displayed by the Lancashire market gardeners. While in the south-east of England it was recommended to be grown 'in great quantities for food for swine and other cattle', or in gardens as a substitute for the artichoke, the Lancastrians were perfecting modern techniques. The setts were chitted in temperature-controlled houses, and either planted in heated greenhouses for sale as earlies, or hand-planted in field drills on old manure, at spacings which are now being reintroduced for 'square planting'. By the end of the eighteenth century the county returned an average yield of $7\frac{1}{2}$ tons to the acre— similar to the modern figure—with the exceptional crop as high as $17\frac{1}{2}$ tons. Here, as in the Netherlands and France and Ireland, potatoes had by now become the principal foodstuff of the working classes—so much so that when blight struck the crop, as it did in 1845, 1846 and 1848, it was a national disaster both in Ireland and on the crofts of Scotland and the Western Isles. The diet of the working man's family was certainly monotonous, but neither as tasteless nor as unexciting as a succession of all-potato meals would be today, for the plant breeders had not yet bred out the flavour and the colour and the flouriness in their pursuit of easy peeling, white flesh and eyelessness. Even the varietal names had flavour—the Irish Apple, the Ox Noble, and the Lumper; and these too have long disappeared apart from a few handed down from generation to generation on the crofts of Galway and Donegal, in western Eire. Everywhere else they have been replaced by those insults to a good table, the Majestic and the Home Guard.

The other great development of this period, on the Continent if not in Britain, was sugar-beet. This was ultimately to fulfil the same role in the crop rotation as the potato, a root break in a succession of cereals. From the earliest times honey was the sole sweetener until the sugar-cane plantations were established in the newly discovered Americas; but cane sugar was expensive to ship. In the year 1747, Marggraf, a chemist working in Berlin, evolved a method of extracting the sugar which, for two hundred years, had been known to be contained in the beetroot. Within fifty years a factory was built in Silesia for the commercial processing of beet, and both France and Holland quickly followed suit. For some decades the projects teetered on the edge between success and failure: the husbandry of the beet was not well understood, the transport to take the crops to the factories was often wanting, and the extraction rate and the refining process were far from perfect. But most of Western Europe had overcome these difficulties and had a flourishing sugar-beet industry in existence nearly a century before the first successful British factory was established in Norfolk in 1912, under Dutch control: before this there had been several ill-fated attempts to get the new industry under way.

There were, therefore, in the early years of the nineteenth century all the modern ingredients of the arable or mixed farming rotation to the hand of the farmer, both British and Continental. The fodder root crops for livestock were well established in Western Europe and entering into British husbandry rather slowly. The red clovers had been cultivated in the Low Countries since the thirteenth century, and the technique of their use was known in England in the seventeenth. Turnips were old history in the Low Countries by the time they came into common use in Britain in the eighteenth century; and towards the end of this century mangolds—or mangel wurzels—were moving out of their country of origin, Germany, into France. The swede, or Swedish turnip, was spreading at the same time. All these fodder roots and grasses were high yielding and enabled very effective use to be made of the break year, or even the few months of a bastard fallow. A continuous cropping programme was now possible for every arable farmer, except a few on the very heaviest of the clays which had to await the invention of heavy mechanical cultivating tackle before they could be brought into condition with any degree of certainty without a rest and cleaning under fallow one year in every three, four or five. The problems that remained to be solved before agriculture took on a wholly modern look were those of field equipment, of more productive crop varieties, of the protection of the crop from infection and infestation, and of cheap and easily handled sources of fertility to supplement (and in time replace) the supplies of farmyard manure and other waste products that were becoming less and less adequate. Of these problems, only the first—the development of more efficient implements of husbandry—made any real progress towards resolution in the early nineteenth century.

Here Britain made its other great contribution to world agriculture, not as large nor as fundamental as its improvement in livestock but none the less substantial. The invention that has captured the imagination is that of the seed drill by Jethro Tull in the early eighteenth century. The importance of this may have been exaggerated, for the greatest benefit credited to the Tull drill was that the setting of the seed in rows enabled later hoeing to be done to clean the crop. At the row widths used, this can never have been very easy nor could it have had any real and lasting effect at the early stage in crop growth at which it had to be carried out. The real benefit may have been the more even spacing of the seed made possible by drilling in rows, as compared with broadcasting, and the constant depth of sowing through the seed coulter compared with covering of the broadcast seed by harrowing. Be that as it may, Tull, like Bakewell, performed a useful service by concentrating the attention of the farmer on finding new solutions to old technical problems, by stimulating his thought, and by breaking his traditions.

Of rather greater importance to the arable husbandman was the progressive improvement in plough design, which enabled stubble or grass to be broken, turned and covered more effectively and faster than had been possible with the heavy wooden implements that had been altered only in detail rather than in basic design over several preceding centuries. The new type of plough seems to have appeared in Brabant in the early eighteenth century in the tentative form of a combined iron share and mouldboard which offered far less resistance to the furrow slice than had Blith's improved English wooden plough of the later seventeenth century. Almost simultaneously in England Stanyforth and Foljambe patented their Rotherham plough in which the heavy framework of the mediaeval wooden plough was discarded and a winding mouldboard was introduced in place of the former straight board. Observant, open and mechanical minds were at last at work. Their approach was exemplified by James Small's work on mouldboard design, in which he reduced to paper the natural curves of earth movement which he discovered by allowing the turning furrow slice to wear away a soft wooden mouldboard. Then he analysed the mechanical forces at work in ploughing and applied his findings to the casting of new implements in iron.

The actual details of improvement to implement after implement are less significant than the arrival, in what must now be called the field of agricultural engineering, of the engineer's approach to problems of soil mechanics, seed placement, harvesting and crop handling. The industrial revolution was seeping out of the new factories of Britain into the old fields. It progressed slowly, of course. A century or more after the firm of Ransomes, Simms and Jefferies began to send out, from their Ipswich factory which in 1843 employed 1,000 men, their iron ploughs in infinite variety through the civilized, and uncivilized, world, it was still not difficult to find a wooden plough made by a local carpenter to traditional design at work only a score or two miles from Ransome's own Ipswich factory; and even today such is not an uncommon sight in Bavaria or Franche Comté. Their continued use is not necessarily primitive or unprogressive: they merely live on in situations where manpower costs and counts for little, and the capital cost of an expensive new tool cannot be justified. It is a dangerous assumption—to which this book is as prone as any other—that novelty is always progress and that conservatism can never be right.

None the less, invention was abroad and infections. Mr G. E. Fussell has compiled a chronological list of farmers' tools. From 1760 to 1800 ideas proliferated and were patented: there were ploughs for drainage and trenching; a dynamometer to measure the forces at work in the movement of the share and mouldboard through the soil; machines for threshing grain to replace the age-old flail; chaff cutters to cut up straw for cattle food. Then, after 1800, engineers turned to solutions of the problem of mechanizing the harvest, which culminated in Britain in Bell's reaper of 1828. This, with its reciprocating cutter bar and side delivery of the cut straw fell little short of the efficiency of the binder which was to hold the field until the arrival of the first combined harvesters in the 1920s: all that it lacked was the binding and knotting mechanism to bind the loose straw into sheaves. In 1841 the Royal Agricultural Society of England held a competitive trial of threshing machines, which had by then developed every feature found in a modern thresher. In 1848, at a second trial, the threshing drums were driven by steam engines; and a year later the steam plough arrived.

It has only just left the rural scene. For a hundred years the procession of traction engines; of trailers carrying the wire hawsers that pulled the heavy iron plough across the field and the winches, pulleys and strakes that handled the cable; and of iron-wheeled caravans in which the steam ploughmen lived— this cavalcade snorting along the lanes was the first sign that the era of animal traction, that had lasted for upwards of ten thousand years, was nearing its end. A slightly differently constituted procession of traction engine, threshing drum, baler and the inevitable caravan spelt the end of the winter work in the barn for the men beating the grain out of the ears on to the floor: it was a finale that was lit by the pyrotechnics of burning stacks and barns as the unemployed and the under-employed men made their pitiful protests against the coming of this envoy of the industrial revolution to the countryside. The battle between drum and flail still lingers in remote parts: in one of the valleys running up from the Herefordshire plain into the flanks of the Black Mountains of Wales at least three men who grew small fields of oats still threshed their crops with the flail into the 1960s.

Again there arises that assumption. Novelty, here in the shape of threshing drum or combine, is progress; and the conservatism of the flail can never be right. It was an assumption that was very dear indeed to the hearts of the improvers in the decades around the turn of the eighteenth and nineteenth century; and even closer to the hearts of their children and grandchildren. It was exemplified at the height of its contempt in that remarkable series of publications, the county surveys published by the Board of Agriculture in the years between 1793, when the Board was founded, and 1818. That very serious gentleman, Sir John Sinclair, explained the background of the surveys to the House of Commons: 'For though in some particular districts improved methods of cultivating the soil are practised, yet in the greatest part of the Kingdoms the principles of agriculture are not sufficiently understood, nor are the implements of husbandry or the stock of the farmer brought to the perfection of which they are capable.' Note the idealist speaking: not brought to the greatest profit, which is after all the motive of all serious commercial agriculture; not made to yield the subsistence for a family, which is the aim of peasant farming; but 'brought to perfection'. Sir John, didactic as well as idealistic, gave no sign of awareness that even perfection is relative when one handles the products of the soil: what might be thought perfect in 1793 had become pretty mediocre by 1843 and an historical curiosity by 1893. The estimable Secretary of the Board, Arthur Young, was equally unaware of the financial balance sheet of agricultural progress. None the less, despite the naïve idealism and gullibility, these surveys were the most important contributions yet made to the knowledge of agricultural practices in Britain. More indeed than agricultural practice, for the author of each county report (or,

in Wales, regional report) analysed nearly every aspect of rural
life from workers' cottages to forestry and from mechanical inventions and usages to the incidence of tithe. Few reports, either
in the draft form or after revision, stand up to critical dissection.
Even Mr Secretary Young's apparently complete picture of
Hertfordshire, for example, turns out to be based upon a few
statistics and upon interviews with ten or a dozen landed or
farming notables. But nowhere before, except in the pages of
Young's own provincial *Tours* and in Marshall's regional *Rural
Oeconomies*, had there been anything approaching the detailed
descriptions and examinations of husbandry as some of the best
and a few of the worst farmers practised it.

These leather-bound octavo volumes must have had a considerable circulation for they are commonplaces on the shelves
of the antiquarian bookseller. This was merely another manifestation of the late eighteenth-century thirst for agrarian knowledge, a thirst that had arisen quite suddenly in the second half
of the century and which the small army of agricultural publicists
commanded by Young and Marshall found it mentally—and
perhaps financially—profitable to quench. The thirst took many
forms. Some were national like the Board of Agriculture itself,
a quasi-governmental body equivalent to a standing committee
today. Some were local, like the proliferation of provincial
societies which often included in their title the phrase, for the
advancement and the encouragement of agriculture. The Bath
and West Society was founded in 1777 to publish papers, conduct
trials and hold shows; the Highland Society followed in 1784,
the Kent and Cornwall Societies in 1793, and a dozen more
before the end of the century. Young's own *Annals of Agriculture*
were the first, and one of the best, of the farming journals; and
a successful *Farmer's Magazine* began to appear in 1800. These
were the decades of the great flowering of agricultural self-help,
which culminated in the founding of the Royal Agricultural
Society of England itself in 1843 and of the Royal Agricultural
College at Cirencester and the Royal College of Veterinary Sur-
geons in London, and the establishment of a number of journals to
which some still existing papers can trace their origins, *Farmer
and Stockbreeder* for example, and the *Gardener's Chronicle*.

Ernle, in his splendid classic *English Farming Past and Present*, long ago put his finger on the reason for this sudden proliferation of societies, books and journals. Farming had become an immensely profitable calling; the rewards of the soil were sufficient to attract capital investment by landlords and promote a more highly abstractive husbandry in the farmer. But it was the landlord in particular who was most concerned to wring high returns from his farms in hand and high rents from his tenanted holdings. So universal was the pursuit of agricultural knowledge among this class that even the merchant foxhunter aspired to publish 'Mr Jorrocks on Short'orns'. The prime causes of this agricultural prosperity in Britain were the wars and protection. From the Stuart Restoration in the seventeenth century it had been the aim of government to prevent grain 'from being at any time either so dear that the poor cannot subsist or so cheap that the farmer cannot live by the growing of it'. During most of the period, therefore, imports of grain were regulated so that the British farmer was encouraged to grow as much as he could and the market was stabilized by an export bounty in times of glut and controlled imports when harvests failed. But towards the end of the eighteenth century it became obvious that the farmer was falling behind in his race to keep production abreast of the soaring industrial population, and foreign supplies had tended to become depressed by the closed door into Britain. The Napoleonic Wars exacerbated this situation to the point where wheat made a steady 120s a quarter as compared with a pre-war average of 45s (the current, 1965, guaranteed price for wheat in Britain is 120s a quarter). This, together with higher prices for other farm produce, was the incentive to perfect the techniques of husbandry, enclose nearly the last of the remaining open fields and commons, and improve estates to encourage tenants to pay the higher rents which their prosperity permitted.

The boards and the societies, the surveys and the journals, were the reflection of this trend in meeting hall and show ground, in study and printers' shop. In the process, the relics of primaeval countryside, the last shreds of mediaevalism and the vestiges of subsistence agriculture were swept away, so that when the wars ended Brougham could say that 'not only have wastes disappeared

. . . giving place to houses, fences and crops, but even the most inconsiderable commons, the very village greens and the little strips of sward by the wayside been cut up into cornfields in the rage for farming'. He exaggerated, of course: several small wars and two great wars since have not succeeded in bringing some small parcels of waste in most parishes into cultivation. But he might have added that the plough had gone up the hillside and into other like places where it had never been before, and sometimes was never to go again even between 1939 and 1945. When the war ended at Waterloo, the famous—or infamous—'landlords' Act of 1815 sought to perpetuate wartime prices into peace, and indeed succeeded in keeping returns at a level high enough to maintain agricultural prosperity until the Corn Laws were repealed thirty years later—and even beyond that time. The Act was defended by Liverpool, the Tory prime minister, as an attempt not to protect the landlord but to secure a regular domestic supply of grain. The validity of the reason advanced by Liverpool was very real. There was a rise in population because of a trend to earlier marriage, made possible by high industrial wages, and a continuing fall in the death-rate; and there was more money about to be spent on food. Both factors made the demand for farm products, and cereals in particular, increasingly difficult to meet.

This, and the consequent high profits, were the two stimulants to the improvement in the techniques of husbandry and to the reclamation of most of the remaining waste land in Britain. Despite some recession in the period 1820–28, the whole of the century from 1750 to 1850 was one of comparative boom in farming everywhere, with great profit arising from the cultivation of cereals and only a little less from the grazing animal. The plough went in everywhere: into the new-made polders of Holland, into the heaths of Luneberg, into the hillsides of Wales, even into the pastures of Ireland where in a quarter of a century 200,000 acres came newly to the plough from old grass or even older bog. It is commonly concluded that livestock numbers fell dramatically: this view is in error. The plough does not always banish the hoof, it merely sustains it in a new way; and the alternate husbandry of the cereal-roots-grass rotations changed the methods of the stock husbandman rather than sent him out of business. Hitherto grass and stock had been synonymous. Today grassless stock husbandry is a commonplace in the barley beef-lot and the maize-silage fed dairy herd. The early nineteenth century witnessed the beginning of the change when, on many mixed farms, the grass and turnip breaks replaced fallows in the intervals between cereal crops. These began to make possible a new, intensive type of stock husbandry.

CHAPTER EIGHT

The World as Europe's Larder

The years from 1850 to 1939 saw the eclipse of the countryman in the more highly industrialized nations of Western Europe. The eclipse was at its fastest and most complete in Britain where, in 1851, only $1\frac{3}{4}$ million of the population of 21 million worked on the land, or one person in every five at work. A measure of the effectiveness of Britain's agriculture was that it still grew most of the nation's food, as, six hundred years ago, it had also grown the nation's food. But in 1250 there were probably $2\frac{1}{2}$ million, and the dividing line between surplus and scarcity was so fine that national semi-starvation lowered resistance to the plagues which were sweeping Europe one after another. In 1851 the size of the national harvest could still be critical; but a new factor, the rapidly increasing imports of food which the end of protection was allowing to enter, ensured an adequate supply.

The Corn Laws, which had provided a home market for all the grain the arable farmers of Britain chose to grow, were repealed in 1845 under pressure from the Whig industrialists whose interests lay in free trade for their manufactures and in cheap food, preferably taken in exchange for their exports, for their workers. The Whig case was one which, in the circumstances of the time, it was difficult to attack and easy to defend; and, indeed, apart from the emergencies of the two world wars of the twentieth century it has never been convincingly shown that the emphasis on industrial production at the expense of an unprosperous agriculture has been wrong. In 1845 it was argued that the protection of cereals was a scarcely concealed subsidy for the landlord, whose rents moved in relation to the profits from farming. The point had substance. It was further argued that it was up to the home farmer to become competitive with the foreign farmers whose threat to undercut him was just visible on the economic horizon. This also had no easy answer. The advantages of the foreign producer—who was mainly the man ploughing the vast prairies of the New World—were those of scale of operation and untapped stores of fertility. The American wheat grower was unhampered by small hedged fields ill-adapted to the new techniques of mechanization; and he need have no recourse to the complexities of the rotations which were necessary to restore fertility to soils being cropped, perhaps, for the fifteen hundredth time, or to folded sheep and yarded bullocks, both extravagant in labour.

In time one British answer was discerned by a few men: the reduction of costs of output by increasing the scale of enterprise and perfecting the mechanics of production. In fact, in 1849 Sir Robert Peel, whose tariff reform policy had given rise to the problems, was already offering a solution to his own tenants in the form of investment grants for drainage and other improvements. A hundred years later a British government again seeking to underpin its national agriculture was to produce no better answer than similar production grants to finance the farmer's efforts to become internationally competitive. The second answer to foreign cereal competition was scarcely apprehended except by that very wise man James Caird, who maintained that the British farmer should turn from easily transportable and vulnerable crops like wheat to those less suitable for long hauls, such as milk, vegetables, potatoes and sugar-beet, which the rising standards of living of the working classes were now placing in greater demand.

The Corn Laws were repealed to take effect in 1846. At first nothing very disturbing happened. Even though the American and Russian railways moved further out each year into virgin corn-lands shipping costs did not begin to fall until the 1870s, and imports of whole wheat and flour into the United Kingdom rose only slowly, to 35 million cwt in 1865–69 and 47 million cwt in 1870–74. In the latter period freight charges were reduced by the improvements in railways and steamships and in ten years the cost of shipping grain from New York to Liverpool tumbled from 5s 6d to 2s 11d a quarter. Exports of wheat from the United States correspondingly rose from 59 million bushels in

1870–74 to 136 million bushels in 1880–84 (and to 184 million bushels by the end of the century). Peace also began to play its part: after the decades of the Crimean and Franco-German wars trade was unleashed and Russian wheat exports were nearly doubled in the twenty years from 1870.

British arable farmers who had been so completely protected by import restrictions, transport costs and the hindrances of war were suddenly left defenceless. The average 35 million cwt of wheat which the United Kingdom had imported in the years 1865–69 rose to 92 million cwt in 1890–94, imports of barley rose from 7 million cwt to 20 million cwt, oat imports doubled, and a new factor was introduced in a virtually new import of 35 million cwt of maize for the animal feeding-stuffs market which had previously been supplied by the home producer of cereals. The effect was to reduce the price of wheat to one half in thirty years and of barley and oats to about two-thirds. Not until the last two or three years of the nineteenth century did the prices received by the British producer begin to rise again slowly as the American grain farmer exhausted his stores of virgin fertility. The average income of the British farmer did not fall in direct relation to the catastrophe—as it seemed to him—which befell him in the local corn exchange every market day, as the merchants' interest in his sample bags dwindled and as their prices for his cereal harvest became more and more derisory. J. R. Bellerby has calculated the movements of farmers' 'incentive incomes', that is, the reward for management left after rent, wages and interest on invested capital have been met. This national farm incentive income fell from £40 million in 1867–78 to £24 million in 1879–83 (but it rose to £47 in 1906–14 because rents and wages increased again far more slowly than the prices for farm products).

But the disasters of the grain market and total farm incomes did not move precisely in step because the cereal producer was really only a minor figure on the British scene. T. W. Fletcher, the Manchester farm economist, has brought the picture into focus recently by pointing out that even at the peak of high Victorian farming wheat accounted for only thirteen per cent of the gross agricultural output of the United Kingdom. The cries of calamity that rang through rural Britain were in fact merely the last echoes of the sixteenth-century credo that shepherds be ill archers, that the grazier was of little moment in the human ecology of the countryside, and that a prosperous rural Britain and a prospering arable agriculture were synonymous. A Royal Commission appointed in 1879 was manned by landlords and large arable farmers who concluded that corn was vitally important, that all England was distressed, and that the major cause of the depression was a succession of bad seasons. As Michael Tracy has written in his masterly analysis of agriculture in Western Europe in the past eighty years, the Commission did not see that a fundamental change had taken place in the pattern of world trade and that a corresponding adaptation in British agriculture was necessary. A second Royal Commission, reporting in 1897, succeeded in recognizing the competition from foreign grain as the chief and enduring enemy of the British arable farmer; declared itself resigned to further reductions of the arable acreage, production of grain and rural population; and offered no remedies except relief in the incidental burdens of the farmer—rates, tithes and transport costs.

In the meantime, the livestock husbandman was suffering a comparatively small diminution in his livelihood. The value of the output of livestock products actually rose by ten per cent in the last quarter of the century, due mainly to an increase of one-third in milk production. Added to this was a marked reduction in the cost of feed caused by the low price of imported feeding grains. Imports of beef increased ten times between 1865 and 1895 and increased another three times in the next fifteen years; imported mutton, negligible in the earlier year, rose to over 4 million cwt a year in the first five years of the twentieth century; and butter, cheese, eggs and wool all showed manifold increases. But milk was not, and has not yet become, an importable commodity; and the hallmark of the period was the rapid and great change of a population of mainly mixed farmers into a nation of milk producers. Royal Commissions might be blind, but Scotsmen in particular were quick to weigh up the situation, snap up the thousands of arable holdings falling vacant and derelict in the south-east and around the towns of the Midlands and the North, stock the broken-down pastures with cows, and turn the proud yeomanry of England into an army of cow-keepers. The introduction of economies of scale into arable husbandry had been one, less common, answer to the Great Depression; this voluntary embracement of what Caird had called 'the skilful use of new advantages' was the second effective answer.

Many more improbable and mainly unpromising answers were propounded by economic theorists and amateur politicians. The opposition to Free Trade crystallized into a Fair Trade movement, promoted by the National Free Trade League, whose principal platforms were moderate import duties on food, with Empire preferences, and retaliatory tariffs against the protectionism which European countries in general resorted to as a shield against the flood of grain from America. The battle for protective tariffs to help the British farmer raged in varying degrees of ferocity for half a century and culminated in the concessions of the 1930s; but it was scarcely half a victory: both flanks were still wide open, for the British Empire itself, for which preferences were proposed, had become one of the main competitors of the British farmer.

The failure of the farming platform was foredoomed. The electorate was shown by each decennial census to be growing more urban and industrial, less rural and agricultural; and ninety-five per cent of the voters—with the minute exception of a few idealists—were vitally interested in cheap food. As always, the farmer continued to be his own worst enemy in public relations, whining or vituperative in adversity, arrogant and and stiff-necked in prosperity; and he and his few friends still resorted to the mystic ethic of wheat as the cornerstone of a country edifice in which there was worshipped the sacred cow of a corn law. The other base of his argument, home-grown food as the first line of national defence, seemed to be invalidated by the productive capacity of the British Empire and the strength of the British Navy. He even failed to speak effectively, or with one voice. He had to rely upon the shrinking shadow of his landlord to promote his cause in Parliaments, where the rural seigneurie was a red rag to the majority of bulls which represented the industrial towns. These spokesmen of his, dismissed by most people as reactionary anachronisms, put their own interpretations upon the reasons for the arable disaster, and they were usually the wrong ones. And a succession of farmers' associations, beginning with the Central Chamber of Agriculture in 1865, proceeding through a Farmers' Alliance of 1879 and a National Farmers Union of 1908 (which remained politically inept and nearly powerless for thirty years), were usually divided in their policies and devoid of influence. For half a century the British farmer had only two effective answers to his economic problems: to put his corn production on an industrial basis, or to devote himself to those products which had the natural protection of distance and perishability.

It was at this point that the real cleavage occurred between the nature of the rural societies of Britain and of her Western European neighbours. There had long been some differences, both tenurial and technical; the tenurial ones were mainly in favour of Britain, the technical ones often showed a Continental superiority. In France, the Revolution had split the large estates into a vast number of peasant holdings. The agricultural statistics for 1882 showed there to be more than $2\frac{1}{2}$ million farms of one hectare upwards, with another 2 million below one hectare; the average holding was 8·7 hectares (or twenty acres), distributed between twenty-two parcels of land of a size of less than two-fifths of a hectare each. Long leases—indeed, certain security of tenure of any sort—were very rare. The peasants were both tenurially fragmented and mentally static, and they formed more than two-thirds of France's population. It was for these two reasons that the free trade movement, based on the precepts of William Cobden, made virtually no progress for forty years against protection, which was introduced for agricultural products during 1810–20. Then a brief commercial awakening for twenty-five years, from 1860 to 1885, removed most tariffs, but these were promptly restored as soon as the threat of transatlantic grain became real. Even when the exhaustion of the original fertility of the American Middle West restored something like parity to prices of grain on each side of the Atlantic the French tariffs on imported foodstuffs continued until the First World

War. In so continuing they maintained the peasant structure of her farming and a moderate level of prosperity; but they kept at bay all the incentives to modernization which were such a potent economic force in Britain. France's—and Europe's— only contribution to the pool of economic ideas was co-operation.

Why the British farmer notably failed to co-operate in buying and processing and selling as his European contemporaries did has never been satisfactorily explained. The minute farms of Western Europe were one factor which encouraged co-operation; the importance of wine production in which no small producer can hope to survive alone was another. But there were deeper, psychological reasons than these: the greater equality of status among Continental farmers and an absence of the distrust of neighbours' intentions and achievements which the British farmer misnamed his sturdy independence. Therefore when the aristocratically based Société des Agriculteurs de France—an organization founded in 1860 as a compromise between the English Royal Agricultural Society and Farmers Club—mooted the formation of syndicates for agricultural buying and selling, the membership of the new co-operatives grew rapidly to 234,000 by 1890. This was a figure close to the total number of farmers in England today.

The German arable farmer was also in a happier position than his English counterparts. For most of the period during which the American grain threat was greatest he had the shelter of some sort of a tariff wall; and, compared with the French, the German cereal grower was a man of wide acres, technically competent and supported by an agricultural science that was more advanced than that of any other country, Britain included. This was partly a legacy of history, partly an accident of soil type that had concentrated the large cereal farms in the eastern part of the German Empire, where the Junker caste were the nineteenth-century editions of the mediaeval feudal landlord with large estates. Their vast tracts of light soil were one of the major natural grain-growing areas of Europe, perhaps of the world. Another accident, that of war, has now perpetuated this ancient division, with East Germany enjoying a large and easily culti-

French sheephouse at Trembley-le-Vicomte

Tushuri sheep flock in Transcaucasia

Rhiw type of Welsh Mountain sheep

Jersey bull in 1856

vated arable region; and the Federal Republic of West Germany having mainly the small mixed or stock farms, or in Bavaria a peasant structure of tenure with the fragmentation of holdings becoming more intolerable with each generation.

The hesitation with which the German government and the public opinion behind it approached protection in the second half of the nineteenth century stood in a midway position, as it were, between the freedom of trade to which Britain was committed by her urban and industrial emphasis, and the firm system of import tariffs which the predominantly agricultural France developed to shield her large rural population. Germany by the end of the century had just reached the position of having half her people still engaged in agriculture and its allied callings, and half employed in her rapidly growing and highly successful industries. The country had also been a considerable exporter of grain from her Prussian arable farms. As industry became dominant it fought to maintain the position of low or no tariffs on foodstuffs, which had hitherto been the natural policy of the agricultural sector of the nation; but as the great Prussian grain producers first lost their export markets to the Americans and then began to feel the impact of large quantities and low prices of American wheat they began to press for some protection. Germany began to move closer to the economic position of Britain where, a decade or two earlier, the same situation had arisen. In Britain, as has been seen, commercial influence was strong enough to preserve the freedom of trade intact; and even the agricultural leaders were slow to realize that it was neither providence nor bad weather which was ruining them, but simply cheap foreign grain. The Junker retained his ancient powers and his great influence, when the British landed gentry had lost much of theirs; and these German landowners increased both power and influence by combining together in 1893 in a Farmers' League (the Bund der Landwirte). The Bund brought pressure to bear on political candidates and in a few years had succeeded in extracting substantial tariffs on imported grain and some other farm products from the Government. This achievement in the face of the booming commercial and industrial world of Western Germany was evidence of the power still reposing in the hands

of the great seigneurie of the Prussian corn lands. One contemporary—Bürger in his significantly titled *Die Agrardemagogie
in Deutschland*—even described it as 'agrarian terrorism'. And
so it was in some of its manifestations, descending as it sometimes did to commercial boycotts reinforced by physical violence
against its opponents (and particularly Jews), which was a
shadowy forewarning of the Nazi Germany of the 1930s.

Reactionary as such attitudes might be, the Bund sometimes
showed political acumen in advance not only of current German
economic philosophy but also of world political thought. As early
as the mid-1890s it advocated what was in effect a national
monopoly in trading in cereals, with regulated prices and a
reserve fund from which deficiency payments or import subsidies could be paid on occasions of internal over- or under-
production. The proposal was on all fours with the six-nation
plan for the stabilization of Common Market supplies over half
a century later. It fell down mainly because it seemed that the
Bund had overstepped itself in its battle for protection at the
expense of the consumer; and the Junkers had to content themselves with manipulating the complex import-export certification
system which, legally but skilfully fiddled, acted as a devious
subsidy to Prussian grain producers and had, by 1910, come to
be worth 121 million marks to them.

The result of all this power politics and shrewd deployment of
influence was the maintenance of the cereal acreage in Germany
during a period which in Britain witnessed the great depression
in arable farming. Indeed, between 1880 and 1910 the area of
Germany under rye, wheat, oats and barley actually increased
from thirteen million to fourteen million hectares and production
from fourteen million to twenty-seven million tons. But the
financial benefits mainly accrued to the larger farmers, particularly from the receipts from the hidden subsidies, so that the
situation was not unlike that in Britain since the Second World
War, where the barley barons have collected a lion's share of the
cereal support funds.

It was, strangely, the small nation of Denmark which reached,
logically and amicably, an adult solution. Denmark suddenly
grew up at the end of the eighteenth century. Under the inspired

government of Bernstorff a country which had retained a feudal structure of rural society with open fields and villein tenures was turned into a peasant Utopia. The open fields were broken up into holdings of viable size, with the steading in the centre; and these were maintained intact by law. There was then established, from 1784 onwards, the rural Denmark of today; with family holdings kept up to date with government aid and tended with all the pride of ownership, and a system of general and technical education many decades in advance of the rest of Europe. The impact of the transatlantic cereal flood was no less severe here than elsewhere, for the Danish peasant had carried forward the traditions of grain growing as a primary occupation from his recent open field farming. But structurally the country was better placed than any to meet cereal competition; and all levels of agricultural opinion, from the leaders of the Danish Royal Agricultural Society down to the peasant farmer, saw the crisis coming and were preparing to meet it when it came. The emphasis was changed completely, from bread grain growing to livestock production partly based upon cheap imported grains. It was the textbook answer; but no other country in Western Europe apart from Holland and Switzerland was so ready, so fast or so unanimous in giving it. The acreage of animal feed crops was increased, and particularly of roots which the Danish stockman has always used so considerably. Livestock numbers rose fast: cattle from 1,121,000 head in 1861 to 1,706,000 in 1893; pigs from 304,000 to 829,000. Between 1871 and 1903 butter production was trebled, milk production more than doubled, eggs and pigmeat tonnage increased nearly fourfold. The greater part of all these soaring livestock products was processed and marketed by the co-operatives which began to appear in the 1850s and grew so fast that in fifty years there was one to every two parishes for the separation and churning of butter in bulk, a producer-owned bacon factory accessible to every pig-keeper, and 370 societies existing to promote and undertake the export of eggs. Between 1870 and the end of the century Danish livestock product exports rose from a negligible quantity to figures of 70,000 tons of pigmeat a year, 60,000 tons of butter, and 320 million eggs. The most eloquent testimony to the effectiveness of the rationalization and reorientation of Danish agriculture was the steady increase in the number of people engaged in it at a time when in the larger nations of Western Europe men were tumbling out of farming and into industry as fast as they could. It was not even that Denmark had any marked natural advantages as a livestock country: she simply saw quite clearly where her future lay, and moved resolutely towards that goal.

Holland also offered a fundamental answer, and not an expedient palliative, to the sudden change in the agricultural economy of the Western world; and stimulated technical education, co-operation in buying and selling, and the ready provision of finance through Farmers' Credit Banks. Like Denmark she went into the Great Depression with a long tradition of, and a considerable emphasis upon, dairy farming; and like Denmark's, this was based upon grass supplemented by home-grown cereals surplus to internal domestic needs. The change to even more intensive milk production based on heavily fertilized and naturally irrigated grass and cheap imported cereals for feed was easy; and hand in hand with it went the factory processing of milk into butter and cheese in the co-operative creameries which sprang up everywhere with the encouragement first of provincial dairy unions—a form of combined farmers' union and milk processing and marketing board—and then of the Algemene Nederlandse Zuivelbond, now the Royal Netherlands Dairy Union. The result was the maintenance in numbers and prosperity of the rural population and a widespread reconstruction of the dairy farmsteads which lie so thickly over all but the sandy heaths of the Netherlands. So continuous has been the rehabilitation of Dutch farming in keeping with technical and structural (and aesthetic) progress that these sixty- or seventy-year-old farmsteads, with house and byre and barn under one roof, wear an antique look, whereas in any other country of Western Europe with its slower tempo of rural reconstruction they would appear only slightly old-fashioned.

The pattern of technical and economic change in Switzerland was similar, but less rapid and less profound. On the mountain pastures—and no part of the country is below 633 feet above sea-level—farming had always been irrevocably committed to dairying, with some cereal and wine-growing in the midland plain; and the pace of technical change was limited by difficulties of access and of intensification. But by leaving the structure of her dairy farming intact in its ancient cycle of transhumance between valley village and Alpine pasture and introducing co-operative creameries into every community, with a marketing chain leading steadily upwards to increasing exports of preserved milk and cheese, Switzerland weathered the storm of the late nineteenth century with ease, and with a comparatively minor fall in her population activity engaged in farming: in 1888, 475,000 people were so occupied; in 1920, there were still 457,000 people pursuing an agricultural calling.

If a fundamental reason is to be sought for the agricultural revolution in the Western world in this period, it must surely be found in developments in communications. Externally, these brought the agricultural produce of the whole world to the ports of the industrial nations, with all the consequences that have been discussed above. Internally, the change wrought by the network of railways, the postal services and the electric telegraph were such as to destroy the last vestiges of isolation, both material and mental, that had existed since human settlement began. These relics of self-subsistence, to be found in almost all aspects of life, were by no means insignificant or unimportant. The older historians frequently overstated the remoteness and stability of mediaeval society: there was much movement among men of rural affairs, the stewards of estates, the administrators of the monastic granges, the drovers of stock, even the villeins engaged upon their obligations of porterage between manor and abbey or castle. Ideas and news flowed freely, though slowly, through the upper strata of agrarian society; material things less freely. But the historian has also often tended to play down the persistence of the closed shop in rural thought and in rural affairs even into the nineteenth century. The farming journals played no part in transmitting ideas or informing the livestock and cereal man of trends in national and regional market prices until the railways made rapid delivery of the weekly issues both possible and cheap. After about 1840 there was a sudden surge forward in factual communication: yesterday's London *Mark Lane Express* could be read in Bristol today, and discussed at the market ordinary in the Swan at Wells tomorrow. It would have been tedious and impossibly expensive for even the broad-acred barley and sheep man from Dorset to join in the interplay of ideas and watch the demonstration of new stock and new techniques at Mr Coke's annual gathering at Holkham in Norfolk more than once or twice in his lifetime, if at all. By 1850 he could travel cheaply and quickly to the Agricultural Society of England's annual show at Exeter, and go to the Windsor show next year, and the Lewes show the year after if he so desired.

The most profound impact of better communications was on livestock. For centuries the only remunerative outlet for the 'black cattle' that were bred and reared in the glens of Strathspey and on the shores of Loch Awe had been the English midland and home counties and East Anglian feeders, to whom they were delivered by drovers who marched the stock southwards, slowly and with much loss of flesh. These drovers months afterwards returned to Scotland with drafts that could often only be nego-tiated at a considerable discount. By the middle of the nineteenth century the transport of fat—not store—cattle by train or steam-ship from Aberdeen direct to the butchers buying at London Smithfield became a matter of days, not weeks and months; soon the meat went south on the hook, not on the hoof; and the cheque in payment was in the post by return.

The same free wind of modern commerce also began to blow through nearer marts than Falkirk Tryst and Dolbenmaen and Tregaron, the gathering points for driven stock from the Scottish highlands and isles and the mountain pastures of Wales. From Saxon days, if not from Roman and before, markets had grown up spontaneously to bring together the man who had something to sell and the man who might want to buy it. Trade at these embryo marts, the Chipping this and Market that of the English countryside, in time became regulated by custom and by the regulations of the owner of the market—lord of the manor or borough authority—who had obtained the Royal charter granting him, or confirming him in, possession. Throughout this long period, a thousand years or more in the case of the oldest markets, transactions had been by private barter: between the cattle rearer and the drover or butcher, between the housewife with her eggs and butter and the merchant, between the cereal grower and the corn dealer. Then, simultaneously, or nearly so, with the rise of the railways, the auctioneer sprang into importance as the professional, intermediate bargainer between seller and buyer; and within a few decades all large livestock except horses offered for sale at a British market was sold by public auction and not private bargain; and only the farmwife's produce remained a matter for neighbourly haggle. The change was no coincidence, but a logical consequence of better communications. New markets sprang up at railheads—Lockerbie for the Border sheep, Craven Arms for the Hereford cattle of the Marches, Crewe for Irish stores—and the old markets served by the new railways—Banbury, Norwich and Salisbury among them—grew manifold. Buyers could be attracted from further afield than the small radius of influence of the old local mart; and the auctioneers performed a useful service, for a reasonable fee, in announcing the stock on offer in newspaper advertisements and hoardings and in ensuring that the new race of dealers, with cattle trucks waiting in the sidings behind them, had ample choice of stock in large and level lots. The rationalization destroyed the picturesqueness of the random penning and tethering of cattle and sheep along the High Street and the good humour and bad tempers, the chaff and the abuse, of the old days. Such is now found only in the small towns of Eire, and even there it dies fast before the new auction marts of the farming co-operatives.

New communications also opened up a whole new world to the dairy cow-keeper. Indeed it was nearly responsible for the manufacture of the British milch breeds of cattle. Hitherto, the dairy farmer who was more than an hour or two's drive in a horse and cart—ten or twelve miles—had had no market for his liquid milk. He had perforce to make it into cheese or butter, which his wife sold at market and kept the proceeds for her housekeeping, and to feed the whey or skim to pigs. This had been the major occupation of farmers in all the great dairying areas from Wiltshire to Suffolk and Lancashire. Such milk as the townsman drank, which was little by modern standards, was produced in the town dairies. These were groups of yards and byres scattered not only through the outskirts but often in the centre of towns as well, where flying herds of cows were fed upon hay, roots, cut grass and such by-products of urban industries as brewers' grains—a flying herd is one in which cows are bought as they come into milk and are sold when they dry off, to be replaced by yet more down-calvers or newly calved cows. With such a system a high yield of milk was necessary to leave a profit; the cost of feeding was high compared with country cows which milked off grass, which cost little except the rent. And a propensity to fatten was desirable, because the dry cow was normally fed quickly and sold to the butcher. In both cases—the country herd producing summer milk off grass, and the town herd fattened for meat after a year in milk—the ideal was a dual-purpose animal which would both milk well and fatten fast. The single-purpose dairy cow would have been a liability at the end of its service as a milker. The railways, even if they were not wholly responsible for changing this specification for a profitable cow, played a major part in amending it.

The other influence at work was the increasing consumption of milk per head by a population that was increasing at a greater rate than ever before. In the twenty years from 1851 to 1781 the population of Britain grew from less than twenty million to more than twenty-six million—a twenty-five per cent increase in less than a generation. More of these people lived in towns, divorced from all opportunity to milk a cottage cow. And they enjoyed a steadily rising income. At the same time, under the pressure of legislation—the Adulteration of Food Act was passed in 1872—standards of hygiene rose; methods of milk production became cleaner with the introduction of metal churns and of the surface cooler which, by rapidly lowering the temperature of newly drawn milk, prevented harmful and souring bacteria from breeding and prolonged the keeping period. Growing pressures on urban space also squeezed out many town dairies, already hard hit by the repeated outbreaks of cattle plague which beset the mid-nineteenth century. It only needed the introduction by the railways of milk trains from railheads in the dairying counties, and the appearance of urban dairy companies which grew into such great combines as the Express and United Dairies, to open up a new field of profit to the country cow-keeper. As the market and the communications developed the prices of cereals were also beginning to fall under pressure of New World imports. In, historically speaking, the twinkling of an eye Britain turned into a nation of milk producers and milk drinkers.

The phenomenon was peculiarly British. Holland and Denmark had a long tradition of dairy husbandry and a relatively high consumption of liquid milk—but nowhere near as large as the British figure soon became—but France and Germany were, and remained, milk processors rather than drinkers. To this day the bottle of milk is a rare sight in these countries; and a German agricultural adviser, visiting Edinburgh in 1960, declared that to him the most remarkable sight in that city was the pint or two of milk delivered to every doorstep every day.

It was an unusual coincidence of town and country that caused the first fully developed single-purpose milch cow to be the Ayrshire of Scotland. By the middle of the nineteenth century 'the dense population of Paisley and Greenock, and also of Glasgow'—note the order of importance then—took all the milk that the surrounding pastures could produce. The Scots, like the pastoral Welsh, had an old-established dietary of milk and oats, the products of their crofting agricultures; and when they settled in the new industrial towns took their preferences with them. The Londoner, who was the English equivalent of the dweller in the Clyde conurbation, had no such tradition: he looked to meat, ale, bread and cheese. The Ayrshire breed, established from an amalgam of local types of cattle crossed with Dutch-descended stock, provided a thrifty milch cow to supply the milk drinkers of the Clyde towns. These Ayrshire cows, which yielded 900 gallons under reasonable management, were exhibited at work to an admiring public who thronged the spectators' gallery in the 1820s and 1830s in Harley's model cowshed in Glasgow, and were never in the early days impeded by breeding for show points. The nearest English competitor—

the Welsh never had a serious one—was the Shorthorn, an animal which began promisingly and then passed into showmen's hands. Selected out from the maze of families which filled the pages of the old livestock histories—the Foggathorpes and Duchesses, the Barringtons and the Wildeyes—the Dairy Shorthorn became the common cow of the English countryside, and reigned without serious opposition from the beginnings of serious milk production in the mid-century to the 1920s. In its colours of red and shades of roan, it was an attractive and workmanlike animal, but it had been depleted long before of its milk potential; and the pedigree pride saw to it that milk was not bred back into it. In the end—though this is looking ahead of this chapter—the efforts of breeders to breed milk back from within the Dairy Shorthorn ranks themselves have relegated the breed to virtual insignificance. Shorthorn men, conning their pedigrees and keeping the herd book closed against all innovation, worked hand in glove with that unformulated, usually unrecognized law of livestock history: that a breed entering on its career with a fair degree of homozygosity, grows like an empire through youthful vigour to mature strength, and then relapses into effeteness. Such happens in all closed strains: in human aristocracy as in potato varieties, in apple cultivars as in milch cattle and sheep.

In Britain the Shorthorn breed reigned without serious opposition in the late nineteenth and early twentieth centuries. But two enemies were already infiltrating, by invitation like Vercingetorix's to the Saxon chiefs. And these two, the Jersey and the Friesian, in the course of time were to supplant the older breeds of Britain—the Shorthorn, the Ayrshire, the Longhorn and the Gloucestershire—as the country's principal dairy cows: not only the breeds of Britain, indeed, but those of all the nations of the world whose farmers were occupied in commercial milk production. Of the two, the Jersey (with its cousin the Guernsey) was the first to be imported to found pure-bred herds. The Friesian reappeared slowly in the late nineteenth century, two or three hundred years after it, or a related type, had been brought to England, crossed with the native breeds to originate the Shorthorn, the Ayrshire, the Longhorn and perhaps the Hereford, and then disappear from history again after a brief sojourn as commercial stock in Kent and the eastern counties. These seventeenth-century 'Dutch' herds flit through the pages of contemporary chronicles, in vague allusions rather than specific reporting, and then are heard of no more.

The Jersey has been thought to be an exotic among European breeds of cattle; it may well epitomize in its small frame one of the most ancient and distinctive races of cattle. One current theory, based on work in blood-testing by Bangham at Cambridge, is that the Jersey descends from an African or Asian type of mealy-muzzled stock which on its passage through Europe left traces of its characteristics and its uncommon haemoglobin 'B' blood in many French breeds; and finally fetched up in the little island of Jersey where centuries of selection and close-breeding for the attractive fawn colour brought into dominance the linked character of high butterfat milk. Eric Boston has also traced the type through northern and central Africa and it is noteworthy that the Jersey's mealy muzzle reappears in the reconstituted aurochsen at Munich. The comparatively new science of blood-grouping, in suggesting this chain of relationship on the basis of similarity in blood type, opens up a new vista in livestock history, and especially for sheep in which the complexities of ancient relationships—and even some modern ones—may be resolved by this method. The Jersey cow itself has been a particular victim of the breeders' attention. Basically the workmanlike and most thrifty little animal she has become again in commercial hands in Denmark and New Zealand, she has been so subjected in Britain to fantasies of selection for fashionable but useless show points as to be nearly ruined in the post-war years. Fundamentally a producer of large quantities of rich milk in return for only a little food, and healthy and unusually long-lived, she has survived, but only just, the efforts of fanciers to turn her into the bovine equivalent of a French poodle. That would have been a sad end for one of the three best breeds of cow in the world.

Despite the assertions of some of its supporters that the Friesian or Holstein cow is merely an improved version of the one that came out of the Ark, the origin of this black-and-white breed of cattle as we know it is as uncertain as that of the Jersey. The phrase 'Dutch cow', so freely used before the nineteenth century, covered at least the three types that were differentiated in the reorganized Netherlands Herdbook in the opening years of the twentieth century. These were the M.R.Y. (Maas-Rhine-Yssel, after the three rivers which watered its homeland), a large red-and-white cow of heavy milk yield, large size and rapid growth; the Groningen, a black and beefier animal with a distinguishing white face; and the Holstein-Friesian, the black and white which has begot the British Friesian and North American Holstein of today. It was almost certainly 'Dutch cattle' of the M.R.Y. type that originated the Shorthorn and later the Ayrshire in Britain; and probably 'Dutch cattle' of the Groningen type that Lord Scudamore crossed to produce the progenitors of the Hereford. The black-and-white Holstein-Friesian is said by Professor D. L. Bakker to have developed during the nineteenth century from stock brought from the Jutland peninsula to the Low Countries, to replenish Dutch herds decimated by epidemic after epidemic of rinderpest.

The Netherlander, with his long tradition of skilful cow management, fixed and bred on these 'large and lean Danish black-and-white cows', as contemporaries called them, to produce a uniform breed of high milking and beefing powers, successfully and in large numbers. More than half a million of these animals were exported in the three years 1862–64 to Prussia, Belgium and Britain, and of these more than 300,000 came into British east coast ports from London to Inverness. When accurate import statistics were collected after 1872 the trade was seen to be continuing at around this rate: 351,000 from 1872–76, nearly half a million between 1877 and 1889, and 98,000 from 1889 to 1892. Import regulations varied from unrestricted entry, through import for slaughter only, to the total prohibition which was imposed in 1892 to reduce the risk of bringing in the contagious, endemic diseases of cattle which ravaged the Continent. Most of these black-and-white animals were destined for slaughter—the sight of their being driven up from the London docks to Islington is just within the memory of the oldest butchers. But many of them were in-calf cows which were retained for breeding, and it was the descendants of the thirty or forty Friesian herds that were established in the eastern counties which were the entrants in the first British Friesian herdbook of 1910. In half a century the twelfth or so generations of these black-and-white cattle that had travelled from Jutland into the Low Countries and from the Dutch ports into London and Harwich and Hull were to become the pre-eminent dairy and beef breed of Britain, and of many other parts of Europe and America too. Whence came their remarkable powers of converting food, of which they have always consumed a great amount, into either milk or meat in vast quantity none can yet say; although in time the science of blood-grouping may be able to unravel their remote ancestry. That intuitive amateur geneticist, E. Parmale Prentice, worked out a Roman descent for them; but at the most that must be reckoned not proven.

In the middle of the nineteenth century, when these Friesians were merely a useful Dutch milch breed, the most advanced dairy husbandry of Western Europe, and therefore of the world, was practised in the two small countries of Holland and Denmark. But when the British farmer turned his attention to liquid milk sales for townspeople he drew level and then quickly overtook the cow-keepers of these two countries. This was not because he was a better cowman, but merely that the size of the holdings of the bigger milk producers in England in particular gave them all the advantages of a large enterprise in which mechanization, the development of specialized buildings, and the knowledge of the new science of animal nutrition could all be given full play. This, of course, is not to say that Britain became a nation of skilful cow-keepers overnight: far from it. But while the small dairy farmers of Wales and the Pennines pursued their traditional ways into the pitiless slavery of the family farm, or into the bankruptcy court, a sprinkling of progressive men turned the ancient art of extracting milk from a cow's udder into an efficient factory process, with all the precision and efficiency of the very best of the factories. It was the first section of agriculture to feel the hand of the new race of production-technicians who, in other spheres, were turning Britain into the greatest manufactory in the world. The first aspect of dairy husbandry to be affected was the tedious chore of milking itself. The ancient way had been to grip two of the cow's four teats in the clenched hands, opening and closing the sphincter at the top of the teat canal with the thumb and forefinger, and then stroking and pulling the milk down with the other fingers until the udder was empty. Primitive peoples made use of certain milk-ejection reflexes as well, and Professor E. C. Amoroso and Peter Jewell have studied in detail one method still widely used in the Middle and Far East. In this the milkwoman's assistant blows into the rectum or vagina to stimulate the let-down of the milk; and the commonest of insults there is the phrase '*Ya nafahel bugger*' or 'You blower-up of cows'. The custom existed far nearer home in the seventeenth century; for Fynes Moryson, travelling in Ireland, saw women 'put their hands into the cowes tail, and with their mouthes blow into their tailes, that they may draw milk from them'.

When mechanization was first applied to the milking process is uncertain; but one of the first milking machines that worked was an American invention shown at the International Exhibition in 1862, which provoked the *Illustrated London News* to the comment that 'now we are to dismiss the ruddy milkmaid, the poetry of rustic life is being lost'. A decade or so earlier than this, milking machines had been patented in Germany, Denmark and Sweden. Most of them used a vacuum to withdraw the milk in one continuous stream, a more destructive treatment of the delicate tissues and mechanisms of the udder being impossible to imagine. It was realized that some closer imitation of hand milking, or the similar intermittent sucking action of the calf, was needed to make machine milking safe and efficient; and Dr Alexander Shields, a Glasgow physician, joined his anatomical and mechanical talents to the task and in 1895 exhibited the first pulsator at the English Royal Show. This has been refined only in detail, not in principle, over the past seventy years; and has not yet been superseded. By taking two pipelines to the rubber cup placed over the teat, Shields simulated both actions of the hand milker: one vacuum pipe drew the milk out of the orifice at the base of the teat in the same way as the milker's hand pulled it out, and the second vacuum pipe applied a pulsating squeeze

174

and release action to the sides of the teat, similar to the milker's pressure of thumb and forefinger. But even where the milk was drawn mechanically into a bucket, as it continued to be until the 1930s saw the introduction of pipelines to take the milk direct to churns in the dairy, immense problems of hygiene arose. Until steam cleaning of all the parts through which milk flowed came into use—to be followed by chemical sterilization—the keeping quality of milk deteriorated alarmingly. In the old days, a hand milker had merely to wash his hands, the cow's udder, and the milk bucket; and most of the souring bacteria were removed. The complicated teat-cups, pipelines, buckets and lids were less easy to cleanse satisfactorily. The combination of the expense of mechanical milking equipment, the hazards of bacterial contamination, the temperament of the steam or petrol engine that worked the vacuum pump, and the dislike of innovation, made the adoption of machine milking a long process. Even in England and Wales more than a century after the exhibition of the first milking machine, one-tenth of the country's herds are still milked by hand, at the rate of ten cows an hour.

It is doubtful whether machine milking has ever got a gallon more milk out of a herd of cows than hand milking has done; probably it has got several gallons less, saving labour but sacrificing yield. Two other developments that were the very basis of higher milk production were 'scientific' feeding, and 'scientific' breeding. The quotation marks indicate that the advance was in practical empiricism proceeding from theories of nutrition and genetics rather than application of pure sciences to the animal itself. The revolution in breeding belongs to the years surrounding the Second World War; but the feeding of the cow—and other livestock—by *ad hoc* rules developed from the research begun, characteristically, in Germany in the first decade of the nineteenth century. Until then the stockman's eye at the best, or blind tradition at the worst, had dictated which of the available foods an animal should have. Substitute for eye a machine for weighing milk or live flesh, which merely measures more accurately, and practice cannot be said to have changed much. The eighteenth-century dairy farmer noted that milk yields dropped when hay was substituted for cabbages in the winter ration for his herd, and that a flush of milk followed the first grazing of spring grass. Even today, when everything is known about the chemical composition of pasture grasses, no other way of discovering their comparative feeding values has been devised except a crude calculation of the milk that remains unaccounted for after all other factors in production have been credited.

What the first nutrition chemists did was to give comparative, not absolute, values to the common animal feeding-stuffs to enable rations to be calculated by formulae and not by trial and error. It was in 1809 that Thaer, director of the Möglin Institute in Germany, published the results of his investigation into the soluble nutrients in feeding-stuffs and produced tables of their values in terms of hay. The choice of hay as a standard was unfortunate, for it is one of the most variable in quality of all feeds; and even the barley which European chemists have now substituted as a measure proves too inconsistent in the character of its proteins to make it an absolute yardstick. None the less, Thaer did set in motion research which enunciated the principal constituents of feeding-stuffs as proteins, carbohydrates and minerals; determined their functions in the animal's body; then in 1860 enabled Henneberg and Stohmann in Germany to lay down accurately the quantities of each which were needed to maintain the live weight of an animal; and finally to draw a distinction between maintenance and production rations in 1887, and express them in terms of the feeding-stuffs actually used on the farm and not in laboratory terms. This last achievement, by Kellner at the German research station at Möckern in 1905, remained the commonly accepted feeding standard for half a century, and even now is scarcely superseded. Kellner put values of 'protein equivalent' and 'starch equivalent' on all feeding-stuffs; laid down the amounts of each necessary to maintain an animal in bodily condition (the maintenance ration) and to enable it to produce given quantities of milk, flesh or eggs (the production ration); and thus enabled the farmer or his adviser to sit down at his desk and work out the right rations for livestock performing particular functions, from the bullock merely

Fowler's double-engine ploughing tackle

Veterinary inspection, Smithfield, London, 1865

subsisting in the cattle yard to a cow giving five gallons at a milking or a lamb adding half a pound to its body weight each day.

It only remained for the agricultural publicists to spread the gospel of scientific feeding; and this was a half at least of the battle to bring science into the farmstead. No decade, nearly no year, between about 1845 and the end of the 1930s lacked its new prophet of animal nutrition persuading, exhorting or bullying the livestock feeder into some new regimen of diet for his animals. In retrospect, half of them now appear to have been sound enough within the knowledge of their times, a quarter nonsensical, and a quarter fraudulent—for the production and sale of commercially manufactured feeding-stuffs had now begun. The farmer, both British and Continental, had no guidance readily available to him on the comparative values of the 'concentrates' which were sold to him by millers and compounders who ranged from honest through self-deluded to unscrupulous. Some manufacturers of the new oilcakes, now well-known and respected names, were shown by J. B. Lawes at his new Rothamsted experimental station to be selling to unsuspecting farmers for 40s per cwt patent foods of less nutritive value than home-milled cereals costing 8s to 9s per cwt. Despite such warnings, which were rarely permitted sufficient circulation, stock feeders became obsessed with linseed and rape oil cake: 'The favourite feeding stuff of the Norfolk grazier; no matter how dear it may be, he will have it,' wrote Clare Sewell Read, one of agriculture's shrewdest commentators, in 1858. Often it was fed merely to enrich the manure in the bullock yard. The permutations and combinations on the common constituents of the ration—wheat, barley and oats, turnip, swede and mangold, and oilcakes—and the less common kohlrabi, sorghum and maize—were endlessly and inconclusively discussed, and almost always without relating the real or supposed feeding value to the cost. The period has been called the age of the scientific revolution in agriculture: in the feeding of farm animals it might more properly be called the pseudo-scientific revolution—and this pseudo-science has scarcely yet breathed its last.

The two important additions to the diet of farm livestock in

Western Europe were the oilcakes already referred to, and ensiled green crops. The new artificially bred grasses have been included as a third addition; but these were merely improved versions of the natural grasses of the pastures, made leafier, less ready to run to indigestible and valueless stem, and with growing periods that gradually extended the grazing period from late April to early March at the one end, and from early September to late October at the other. Cake and silage were new, very valuable, but capable of misuse. Cattle-cake became so known because it came from the oil crushers' and compounders' mills as large, flat, hard cakes of industrial residues—cotton cake light in colour, linseed dark— which were broken like slabs of treacle toffee in cake-crushers and then added to pulped mangolds and chaffed straw to be fed to everything from strong three-year-old bullocks in the Norfolk beef-yards to dairy cows in the byre and in-lamb ewes in the home paddocks. It began, and long continued, as a gigantic oil extraction confidence trick played by shrewd manufacturers upon a gullible body of men; it took decades to bring common sense in; and the 'cake bill' became one of the farmer's perennial worries.

What the new oilcakes did do was to provide a ready source of protein to add to stock feeds which before had usually been lacking in this constituent. Grass had been a well-balanced nutrient for ruminants, and also for such non-ruminants as horses, pigs and poultry. But winter feeds, even after the intro-duction of roots, were generally short of protein, particularly to meet the needs of growing stock. From the late eighteenth century it became available in increasing quantities after the invention of the Bramah hydraulic press. The main product of the press, oil, was used for lamps, for cooking or for soap, according to the type of seed crushed; but in time, as the oilcake made from the residues from which the oil had been extracted found a growing market, pressing of cotton seed, linseed and soya bean was done for the primary purpose of cattle-cake manu-facture and the oil itself became the residue, albeit a very saleable one. In time new competitors to oilcake emerged; fishmeal, soya-bean flour, artificially dried grass all enabled livestock foods based on ground cereals to be exactly balanced according to the calculated needs of the animal to be fed. With smaller stock kept intensively—the layman's 'factory-produced meat or eggs' —modern mass production methods of chickens, eggs, pork and bacon would be impossible without these foods of industrial, imported or artificially conserved origin. The other essential elements in the intensive ration—vitamins, minerals and some-times antibiotics—have been products of the mid-twentieth century; but the protein element of exotic origin was an innova-tion of the eighteenth century, much discussed by Young and Marshall and all the amateur and professional nutritionists who reported and pontificated upon it so profusely through the eighteenth and early nineteenth century. With rotations and pedigrees, it was a triple King Charles's head of every serious agricultural commentator for more than one hundred and fifty years.

The other addition to the range of livestock feeds, ensilage, arrived scarcely noticed by the mass of farmers in both the Continent and Britain; and remained a stranger to common agricultural practice until wartime shortages caused it to be virtually rediscovered. The process of ensiling, basically one of pickling a green crop either in the acids produced by its own fermentation in the absence of air, or in added acids, had been known from time immemorial. What made it a practical method of conserving fodder on a large scale was the development, in France and Germany in the early years of the nineteenth century, of receptacles in the form of walled silos of sufficient size to hold enough ensiled grass or other green crop to feed a herd of dairy or beef cattle (or occasionally sheep) through the winter. Its slow acceptance, over a period of three-quarters of a century in Britain but rather more quickly among the more advanced farmers in France and Germany, was because of the high degree of skill needed to produce silage of good feeding value. The careless or the ignorant usually found when the silo was opened at the beginning of the winter that it contained a malodorous and poor material which was useless to stock. None the less, a few men here and there who had mastered the art of filling, compressing and sealing the silo continued loyal to the new process. But to the ordinary run of stock feeders, hay, roots and

oilcake were good enough; although prophets like Robert Boutflour, the most dynamic agricultural mentor of Western Europe
in the twentieth century, continually and bluntly told them what
fools they were to stuff good feed and bad indiscriminately into
the mouths of livestock with no thought of fitting the ration to
the productive ability and desired end in milk or meat. 'All of
you are damned jackasses', Boutflour would roar from the public
platform. 'You take good cows and stuff 'em up with your
damned swedes which are ninety per cent water, and wonder
why two thousand gallons of rich milk doesn't squirt out from
the other end. You should be in an asylum.' The ranting and
the roaring, the cajoling and the scientific persuasion had their
effect in the end; and by the beginning of the Second World
War most British farmers knew how to feed their livestock with
balanced and economical rations—even if too often they failed
to practise what they knew. Their slow progress was matched,
if not overtaken, by Danish and Dutch dairy and pig farmers,
who were assiduously educated in animal nutrition by the advisers attached to their farmers' co-operatives; but the other
Western European countries, with their preponderance of
peasant farmers and tiny herds, have been slow to apply modern
methods of feeding.

Most of this progress in the period 1850–1939 attached to
the dairy cow and the pig, both types of animal offering rich
and quick returns for good management: a sound ration fed to
a cow this week produces more milk in the churn next week, a
bacon pig on a balanced diet goes ready to the curers in six
months, not over-fat in nine. Both beef cattle and sheep long
stayed committed to the systems of feeding devised for them by
the eighteenth-century improvers. They were animals in a state
of nature, or nearly so, mainly because the cash rewards were so
long delayed compared with the quick returns from dairy cows
and pigs—and, of course, from the poultry which gave the farmwife her housekeeping money.

Enough has already been said on the British breeds of beef
cattle which had emerged in the early nineteenth century: the
Beef Shorthorn derived from the Dutch cross, the Hereford of

similar origin, the Devon which remained what God and the West Countryman had made it over several centuries, the mainly black breeds of Angus and Galloway bred up from local stock, and the Highland, nearest of all West European cattle to the primitive aurochs. Apart from the black and white—or Holstein-Friesian—of the north-west Continental seaboard, European beef types were still being evolved well into the early twentieth century. The new French breeds were still being fixed, mainly by English Shorthorn crosses which produced sorts as diverse as the Charolais, from a white Shorthorn cross on the local cows of Charole, and the Pie Rouge. These Pie Rouge are often indistinguishable from the red-and-white Dairy Shorthorns which were still imported until recently as a regular outcross on them to maintain the milk yields which tended to fall under undisciplined French breeding methods. The Germans also made some use of the Shorthorn in their Fleckvieh white-faced beef cattle of Württemberg and Bavaria, and rather more use of the white-faced Groningen of the Low Countries. One of the greatest of all the world's breeds of cattle, the Brown Swiss under the various names it enjoys from southern France to the Balkans, had a largely undocumented and unknown history; but it is so distinctive, so obviously genetically homozygous, and so similar to the Jersey cow of proved Oriental origin, that it may be supposed to have a pure descent from the prehistoric types of cattle which moved westwards with immigrants from the cradle of domesticated livestock of the Middle East. Its immense hardiness, its thriftiness in conversion of poor mountain grasses into high yields of milk and rapidly grown meat, its docility and its longevity were all developed through a score or more of centuries of isolation in the mountain valleys of Switzerland. After the black and whites of Friesian type, it is the most numerous breed in Europe today.

As British breeds enjoyed a supremacy, largely well-deserved, in Europe as improvers of local beef cattle, so British methods of beef cattle husbandry came to be models—rather less deservedly—of European practice. The raw materials of the English, and particularly the Midland and East Anglian feeders, were the black beasts from Scotland which now came south by train for sale at local markets instead of on foot for direct delivery to dealers or farmers; to a less degree the blacks from the Welsh hills and the Herefords of the Welsh border; and, increasingly numerous and well-liked, the Irish Shorthorns or Hereford-Shorthorn crosses which by the end of the nineteenth century were coming over from Ireland to the number of nearly three-quarters of a million head a year—nearly two-thirds as stores for fattening, and the rest ready for slaughter. Arrived in England, these strong stores which were often already three years old were fattened on the rich Leicestershire pastures which could finish a bullock to the acre in summer, or in boxes, sheds or yards in the arable counties of the east where the profit—so it was alleged—remained only in the farmyard manure which they left behind them to enrich the root crop break of the Norfolk four-course rotation, which was still nearly universal. A Norfolk box-feed bullock, fattened on a barley and linseed mash and with as little hay as was necessary to keep its digestion in order, was the pride of the Victorian table. There its ribs appeared rolled into layers of fat-marbled lean or its immense buttocks cut into topside or steaks. The great family joint lay as heavily upon the massive table as, later, it lay in the family stomachs. Behind the prime stall-fed bullock, and forked out of the box (or, in the case of less prime beasts, out of the bullock shed or yard) was the rich dung trodden with straw into muck. This was 'made' for another year in great steaming middens, forked into dung carts again, spread by hand on the root break of the four-course, and ploughed in. It may have been the most extravagant possible way of providing plant nutrients, but when the price of the fat beast was added to the value of the organic fertilizers in well-made manure and to the effect of the straw, broken down by bacteria, on the soil structure, the Victorian farmer with his cheap labour may have paid no more dearly for his fertilizers than his grandson does for his granular compounds of nitrogen, phosphate and potash which come so conveniently and expensively in bag or in bulk lorry today. The Victorian expenditure of manpower in indoor beef production would now be untenable, but it was, and is, widely admired in Europe; and in the Pas de Calais and westwards through the Normandy corn-lands great sheds of yoked beef bulls, uncastrated as is the Continental custom, are common enough sights today. These three-year-old red-and-white Normandy cattle, or the gigantic white Charolais, or the more refined but faster growing Limousin, fed to great weight on sugar-beet pulp and barley and soya-bean meal, are the European counterparts of the old English beef which has virtually disappeared from all except the most esoteric of British butcher's shops.

While for a century England's beef techniques were the model for feeders over the Channel, her methods of sheep husbandry found few followers. This was partly because British flocks primarily produced meat, and wool was a by-product; and European flocks grew wool, and meat was the by-product. Like all generalizations, this is not wholly true, but in general the inhabitants of Continental Europe eat very little mutton and lamb and Continental sheep grew fine Merino or Merino-cross wool in preference to fat lambs. British sheep husbandry was also complicated by the multiplicity of breeds it cherished nationally and locally, but the European flockmaster had few of these idiosyncrasies. To him, few sheep were bad sheep; to the Briton no sheep was good except that of his particular choice. And the sheep which lay to the choice of the English, Welsh and Scottish stockman became bewilderingly profuse in the nineteenth century as breeders took the New Leicester of Bakewell and the Southdown of Ellman and Webb and put them on local varieties to breed and fix seemingly endless new types. A whole gamut of Down breeds emerged, each with sufficient difference in function or performance to justify its existence in the eyes of its supporters. The Suffolk, formed from the old Norfolk Horn, made a crossing ram that bred fast growth but slow fleshing in its lambs; the Hampshire, evolved from Wiltshire and Berkshire types, made a crossing ram which got smaller and quicker finishing lambs; and it produced in its turn the Dorset Down, a breeder of slightly larger lambs. The Oxford Down grew out of a Southdown cross on the large and slow maturing Cotswold and sired lambs that made a carcase suitable for large families but too weighty for the smaller households of the mid-twentieth century. In the West Midlands yet another complex of new breeds emerged from the hands of breeders whose motives were partly local loyalties and partly a snatching at the chance of profit from the passion for novelty. The Shropshire Down, the Clun, the Kerry and the Radnor were all made by permutations and combinations of Welsh and West Midland upland sheep and the southern Down breeds. And in the north the bewildering complexity of upland varieties, some often confined to no larger territory than a single valley, were shuffled and redealt in the form of Swaledales, Wensleydales, Teeswaters, Gritstones, Lonks, Penistones and half a dozen other sorts. Even the Black-face, the ancient variety of the Pennines which moved north into Scotland in the nineteenth century, began to evolve subtle and not readily distinguishable varieties in its new homes; and the old white-faced sheep of the Border hills was crossed with Culley's Border version of the New Leicester to produce a wealthier but still hardy new breed of Cheviots, some of which being taken into northern Scotland proceeded to develop into a larger type of North Country Cheviot.

This catalogue, complex as it is, by no means exhausts the new breeds which the nineteenth and early twentieth century developed in Britain; and it ignores the impact of English Down breeds on the old Irish grass varieties. At least half of the new breeds were unnecessary; a quarter of them possessed virtues which were only visible to the eyes of local patriots, who usually claimed that the subtleties of the micro-environments of their sheep grazings were put to fully profitable use only by their own breed. In fact, as the French in particular had always known, the needs of a country with the diversities of climate and pasture of those of Western European regions could be met by only a few types of sheep; and between the two World Wars most British flockmasters made the same discovery. By 1939 the great complex of sheep breeds in Great Britain was being reduced to six types of sheep: the Scottish Blackface and the Welsh Moun-tain, to graze the highest, wettest and most exposed hill pastures; an upland sheep, the Cheviot, to use the lower hill pastures; a breed of crossing ram, pre-eminently the Border Leicester, to sire fat lamb-breeding lowland ewes upon these; a Down breed or two to mate these very prolific and milky half-bred ewes; a thrifty grassland sheep of which the Clun, manufactured from old West Midland moorland types, is the prime example; and an out-of-season breeding sheep for the Christmas and winter lamb trade, to hand in the Dorset Horn which inherits its ability to mate and lamb at any time of the year from some remote Mediterranean ancestry.

This rationalization was brought about by the healthy wind of standardization and simplification that swept through British farming. Of this more must be said later. The intervening period between the emergence of the great mass of new breeds in the mid-nineteenth century and the 1920s and 1930s was one of the extremes in the systems of sheep husbandry which were followed. On the one hand was the labour-consuming hurdled arable flock. This was usually an early lambing Down breed folded over turnips or other roots by means of hurdle enclosures laboriously moved every day by the shepherd so that a new section of the root field could be eaten off and manured by the four-footed dungcart. This was in essence a development of the mediaeval method of folding the dominial or village flock over the stubbles and fallow to bring some fertility to worn out and hungry soils; the nineteenth century merely substituted turnips for the corn stubble and weeds that kept the mediaeval flock on the right side of starvation. The result was particularly picturesque in the strawed lambing folds in which the shepherd of the arable flock kept vigil in his caravan and taught W. H. Hudson and Richard Jefferies his pastoral philosophy. The second great division of British sheep husbandry, the hill flock, changed hardly at all over the centuries except for the introduction into southern Britain of the sheep-dog for gathering the sheep scattered over the hill. It was written in 1870 that 'there are men living who can recollect seeing [in Wales] the natives dressed in running costume for the task of gathering the mountain. Now the Highland sheepdog . . . has made the task a comparatively easy one.' Apart from this, change came slowly, if at all, to the hill flock. It still takes its chance in a bad winter, with many ewes too weak from exposure and starvation to carry a lamb, and with many more dying slow and uncomplaining deaths. For this two reasons are still advanced: that this is the natural way of hill sheep husbandry, and that no other way pays.

The British reputation for being the most skilful flockmasters in the world could scarcely survive examination in this period, although in skilful management the best hurdled flocks had few superiors. Much of Western Europe took greater care of its sheep because there was a continuing tradition of winter housing, inherited from the mediaeval monastic flockmasters. By the early nineteenth century most of Europe was stocked with Merinos or Merino crosses descended from the great transhumant flocks of Spain but modified, in the Rambouillet type especially, from the small, light and fine-fleeced animals of the Mesta into a larger and more heavily fleeced animal. This had been achieved partly by the introduction of a little of the improved English blood but mainly by assiduous and careful husbandry. The Île de France breed of the Paris district was a case in point. It was founded by Professor Yvart, of the École d'Alfort, by a New Leicester cross in the mid-nineteenth century and was exhibited at the French Livestock Concours as the Dishley Merino, for the production of both high quality wool and fat lambs for the Paris winter meat trade. To achieve a high standard of performance, most flocks were housed—as the royal flock of Rambouillets had been housed—in barns or specially built sheepsheds, and there hand-fed an adequate and well-balanced ration of hay, silage, roots and soya-bean. The difference between this careful and painstaking husbandry and the 'natural' existence of the Welsh Mountain breed on their native hills was as marked as it could be.

The Merino was similarly well established in Germany, where the best Merino wools were still being sold by local flockmasters at fairs in the Bavarian towns as late as the period of the First World War; and here again there was a habit of careful husbandry. Such fine-wool sheep were the pride of their national flockmasters; but in northern Europe there persisted a strain of great prolificacy among related types which pastured on the poorer soils from the heaths of the Dutch-German border to the forests of Finland. Known by a great variety of local names —from the East Friesland sheep in the west to the Finnish

Landrace in the north-east—these animals retained, unimpaired by 'improvement', their natural fecundity and high milking powers. They bore, not single or twin lambs, but litters of lambs up to five or more in number, which grew slowly into carcasses which could rarely be 'finished' to the standard demanded by the English table but which became of a lean gauntness fit to slaughter at two or three years of age. Milkiness had also been perpetuated, and encouraged, by the universal European peasant practice of milking ewes for the manufacture of cheese, to the aid of which ancient occupation mechanization in the form of the Swedish Alfa-Laval ewe milking machine finally arrived in the twentieth century. The net result of the preoccupation of the European sheep farmer with the production of fine fleeces from animals of the Merino type or with heavy milking ewes for cheese-making was the protection of Continental flocks from the worst excesses of British breeders, who banished both wool quality and prolificacy and milkiness in their pursuit of fast, fat meat at all costs. Some British improvers were aware of the danger of losing fleece quality; and have frequently tried, from the end of the eighteenth century to the present day, to breed Merino wool into English sheep, but with scant success. Only in the past decade have two or three enlightened breeders in Britain gone into Europe for sheep to restore milk yield to their improved ewes, and with a considerable degree of success. Of this post-war development more will be said later. There has long been a small gourmets' market for fat lamb in Europe, of course, and this was largely met by the Leicester-based Texel breed of Holland that grazed, a ewe under each cow, on the pastures of thrifty Dutch dairy farmers intent on putting every blade of grass to good use.

The modern pig is a peculiarly British product designed for that peculiarly British dish, bacon and egg. The mediaeval types of pig both in Britain and on the Continent developed by selection into lean and slow-growing animals which, by the seventeenth century, were recognizably closer to a modern pig than to the wild swine from which they evolved. Their rapid improvement between then and the mid-nineteenth century was by means of repeated crossing with imported pigs of Oriental origin, and especially with the China and Siamese pig and their descendant, the Neapolitan pig. These improved English pigs derived their colours, red and black, from these sources; and also a habit of rotundity which made them admirable porkers, easily fattened and with a rapid rate of growth. There was much interbreeding with the older white English type which produced a vast array of white and black-and-white pigs of every possible porcine shape. The mixture of genes in the seminal fluids of English stock by the mid-nineteenth century must have been bewildering. Bakewell and others had dabbled in producing a true breeding line, but with little success. Fortunately the pig was as much an object of domestic concern as of commercial importance; and the mid-Victorian cottager had a passion for breeding anything and everything. He ran through the whole range of 'florists' flowers' from auriculas to dahlias and back through tulips to pansies. His aviary was a dazzling chromatic display. He manufactured in this period many of the biggest varieties of onions that have ever lent little or no flavour to soup or steak. And he also manufactured the modern pig.

The credit for setting up a model to which others should breed is usually given to the Yorkshire weaver, Tuley of Keighley, a man who eked out his 18s a week by keeping a few pigs in his backyard. His exhibit at the English Royal Show of 1851 was overburdened with fat to the point of immobility; but as fat bacon was the staple diet of the working man at that time, Tuley's breeding objective was a sensible one—and faithfully followed. At the 1859 show 'scarcely a pig could walk to his trough'. But three factors were soon at work to change the absurdity of the overweight porker into an animal which would slaughter well for more delicate tastes. There was first the insistence by enlightened show judges that, as James Macdonald put it, 'the model pig is one that will in the shortest time and at the least cost produce the maximum amount of lean meat in the best parts, with the minimum of low-priced meat and valueless offal'; and this Tuley's pig would never do. Second there developed, particularly at Calne, what came to be known as the Wiltshire cure, which demanded a long carcase only thinly covered with back fat, light in the shoulder, and heavy in the back legs, which could be lightly cured for delicately flavoured bacon and hams. Third, the Danish farmer and his co-operative advisers seized upon this ideal nearly as soon as the English curers had enunciated it, and proceeded to evolve the ideal pig for the British market to offset the depression of their farming by the cheap American grain.

Capably directed and inherently well disciplined, the Danish pig farmer quite quickly produced large quantities of bacon of consistently high quality which was sold, with a built-in guarantee of satisfaction, over every grocer's shop counter in Britain. This did not just happen, as pig breeding continued just to happen—and happen fairly ineffectively—in Britain. The Danes, under the inspired guidance first of Konsulent Mörkeberg and later of Dr Clauson, worked to a plan. They defined their objective: a pig to produce Wiltshire bacon to sell to their chief customer, Britain. They then examined procedure: three courses were open to them, to use British Large White boars to grade up their indigenous stock, to select and breed up their native Landrace pure, or to breed both Large Whites and Landrace and produce first-cross hybrid sows from them as breeding stock for the commercial farmer. The second method, the breeding up of the native Landrace, was chosen; but there soon came a compromise, with British Large Whites crossing the improving Landrace sows; and this process continued until 1962, when the Danes ceased using the Large White cross. The final result has been the Danish Landrace—the name means merely the breed or race of the country or land—a homozygous type exactly suited to the Wiltshire bacon trade. Unhappily—and this is moving out of the period under consideration—Wiltshire bacon is being superseded and the Dane is being left with a fine but unwanted pig on his hands.

The unimproved Danish Landrace was only one of a white or light coloured type of pig found everywhere in western, central and northern Europe. Among the most widespread was the Mangalitsa of Hungarian origin, with the curious curly white coat found elsewhere only in the British Lincolnshire Curlycoat, now nearly extinct. Two native German white breeds which were standardized into Large White conformation were the Veredeltes Landschwein and the Edelschwein; and in France the Boulonnais underwent a similar transformation. But the Large White was not the only British breed to be used for Continental pig improvement. The Berkshire was imported and crossed on the Normandy pig to make the Bayeux; and it produced the Tigerschwein in Germany and the Goleb in Poland. Here again, British breeders had processed imported raw material into a machine tool of a high precision, to be exported for use abroad; for the Berkshire which the Continent received back had been worked up in midland England from imported Neapolitan stock and from Chinese pigs of immediate European origin. By a further irony, the Berkshire at length won great popularity in its ancestral home in the Far East in its transmogrified form.

From what has been written it may seem that the nineteenth century was especially the age of the breeder, with the ordinary run of farmer trying—or not trying, according to his bent—to keep abreast of or only slightly behind the unprecedented pace of stock improvement. This was largely so; and it was scarcely less true of the breeding of the crops of the arable and grass field. These were at least as important as the evolution of heavy-milking breeds of cows, quicker maturing types of beef cattle and sheep, and pigs of economical and predictable performance. But the new wheats and barleys and clovers were less spectacular than a yard full of fine Angus bullocks, far less obviously a successful innovation to the lay eye, certainly less satisfying to the country gentleman taking his weekend guests on a Sunday morning tour of the farmyard for the glorification of himself and the Almighty, and probably less obvious a significant advance even to the professional eye. Nonetheless, the future lay more with Majestic potatoes, Spratt Archer barley, Squarehead's Master wheat, the Cockle Park mixture of improved grasses, than it did with the Foggathorpe family of Dairy Shorthorns or Mr Stilgoe's Oxford Down sheep; and it probably lay even more with Mr Henry Ford's new internal combustion tractors than it did with anything else; for the natural raw materials of the farm were at the point of subjection to factory-type processes, and method was on the threshold of becoming more important than material.

None the less, it was necessary that the raw material of the arable farmer should be made more productive, as livestock had been made. In Britain, Patrick Shirreff defined the three possible methods of improvement of cereal varieties, as Mörkeberg was to isolate the three choices before Danish pig-breeders. Shirreff looked to natural sports, hybrids and foreign varieties as the sources of better strains of arable crops. Of these, the use of natural sports was as old as the cultivated crop itself: it had been the only way the settled farmer had been able deliberately to modify his crop. Natural selection had sorted out for the shifting cultivator the varieties best suited to any habitat. The sorts of wheat, barley, oats and rye that survived drought or damp or came to harvest in a sunless climate were those from which the following year's seed was naturally saved. Once he had settled, and his cereals had also naturally selected themselves into the types that best suited the environment, the farmer had only one source of improvement open to him, the breeding-on of unusually successful individual plants; those with ears that contained more or fatter grain, or those that carried their ears intact because grains were more tightly held in the glumes when other plants around shed theirs. The method continued un-challenged well into the nineteenth century—and is still of use—for one of the best barleys of the time, Chevalier, came from a single chance-found ear in the French harvest of 1820.

But during the century hybridization gradually took over from sport selection, at first empirically and later, when Mendel's doctrines of inheritance came to be applied by the plant breeder, to a set plan. In Britain, Rowland Biffin at Cambridge set himself to meet the challenge of the American hard wheats which British bakers insisted were necessary to bake a white loaf of bread of high quality. The Americans had derived their bread wheats from the seed merchants of Danzig, the great cereal port of Northern Europe which drew upon the vast arable lands of Prussia. Biffin applied the new techniques of cross-pollination and the breeding on of the promising strains that resulted, using both native and foreign parents. His first success, the quaintly named Little Joss was one-half Russian Ghurka; his second,

Yeoman, actually derived from a cross of the bakers' best-liked
hard wheat, the Canadian Red Fife. On the Continent, cereal
breeding proceeded always abreast of and often in front of British
work; and the intermediate and true spring wheats were entirely
of European origin. They developed in lands where hard winters
made the survival of an autumn-sown crop a gamble—notably
Russia and Sweden. The quest for a European hard wheat has
never succeeded; and those countries which demand a pale and
fluffy loaf still have to rely on transatlantic grain for the greater
part of the grist. In barleys, too, Continental plant breeders
became dominant after the initial British successes with the improved strains of the native Spratt and Plumage varieties. Both
had some centuries of recorded history behind them, but possessed one or more serious faults: the ear shedding its ripe grain
before harvest, a tendency to lodge (or go flat) in heavy rain or
wind, too high a nitrogen content in the grain to malt well for
the brewer, and susceptibility to virus and fungoid diseases of
cereals which had long been the plague of the cereal grower.
The successful new varieties of barley which came on to the
market between the two Great Wars were again mainly the
products of Dutch, French and Danish plant breeders. Similarly, improvements of the principal livestock feeding cereal of
northern regions—oats—were based upon the Poland variety
which was imported through Danzig in the eighteenth century;
and Welsh breeders adapted descendants of this sort to their own
peculiar conditions.

British fodder and other roots were also ultimately of European origin—the turnip from the Low Countries, the mangold
from France, the swede from Scandinavia, the fodder beet and
the sugar-beet from Germany—slowly naturalized to British
conditions. The breeding of crops of the arable field was very
much an international affair, and nearly every variety was of
multi-national origins. The two great exceptions were the potato
and some of the principal grasses. Potatoes, like pigs, were of
cottage dimensions: both were within the breeding capacity of
the allotment holder or gardener. And in the hands of the
amateur, potato varieties proliferated and were lost and rediscovered, named and renamed, to such a degree that it later took

a Potato Synonym Committee several months to elucidate the fact that one sort alone, Abundance, was known under two hundred names. Many of the old titles were picturesque—the Irish Apple, the Ox Noble, the Yam, the Lumper—and many of the old sorts were cherished and perpetuated within the bounds of a few villages. When the commercial breeder took over, however, varieties were reduced to a mere handful for field production; and new criteria were applied. Flouriness gave way to resistance to disease and damage; flavour to yield; cooking quality to a smooth surface for easy peeling.

The concept of grassland farming—that is, the treatment of grass as a cultivated crop and not merely as something which happens to grow—really began with the use in the Low Countries of clovers as a break in the arable rotation. This origin underlines the difference between planned and unplanned pasture. The ley, of one or more years' duration, takes its place in a course of crops, and is sown, used and broken up as part of an overall scheme of cropping. Permanent, or unplanned, pasture is the indigenous grasses remaining *in situ* as a complex sward in perpetuity; and it is modified in only some degree by human agency—the method of grazing, the type of grazing animal, cutting for hay, the application of manures, will alter the composition of the sward but rarely completely change it. The Low Countries leys, which were primarily crops for harvesting seed or hay and only secondarily grazed, were studied by the English travellers of the seventeenth century, and, publicized by a string of authors, adopted to some small extent in Britain, but they did not enter seriously into its agriculture until the eighteenth-century four-course rotations came into common use. Then, by an extension of the period in the rotation in which land was under grass, longer leys of some years' duration developed. This was the alternative husbandry so beloved of the literary agrarianists, and named alternate because the grass ley was broken up for cereal and root crops and then returned to grass to regenerate fertility. Its complex cycles of popularity and disfavour have never been studied, but are none the less quite marked in the agricultural records.

The peaks of favour often follow immediately upon the work of some pastoral prophet. The first of these in modern times were R. H. Elliott and W. Somerville. Robert Elliott was a coffee planter who retired to his estate on the Scottish border in the 1880s, experimented with mixtures of indigenous grasses in four-year leys in an eight-year arable rotation, and proved quite spectacularly that the nitrogen captured from the atmosphere by the clover, the dung from heavy stocking, and the deep-rooting action of the grasses and the mechanical and chemical effects when the sward was ploughed in, together with the encouragement of clover growth by the application of basic slag from the waste-products of industrial processes, all brought a new and heavy fertility to the succeeding root crops. His book, *The Clifton Park System of Farming* (1901), became nearly a Biblical text for a growing number of farmers—some hard-headed, some visionaries, some mystical—who were attracted by the revived religion of alternate husbandry. An equal prophet was William Somerville, professor of agriculture at King's College, Newcastle-on-Tyne, who began the experiments at the college's Cockle Park farm which were to culminate with the preparation by J. W. Gilchrist of the Cockle Park seeds mixture. For half a century this combination of rye grass, cocksfoot and clovers, heavily slagged, dominated advanced grassland practice in Britain, until simpler mixtures for single-purpose leys became fashionable. That the battle of complex against simple seeds mixtures was joined at all before the resurgence of farming after 1939 was evidence of the greater seriousness with which British graziers approached grassland management than did their Continental contemporaries. The issue was partly one of dedication to whatever pastoral god stalked the grass fields in judgment. Simple grass mixtures of one or two varieties, with sharply defined periods of growth and use, were readily maintained in good order; the complex mixture, spreading growth and usage over the season as one after another of its constituent varieties came into flush of growth, demanded a shrewd deployment of grazing stock and the hay or silage mower to keep it productive. Most Europeans evaded—or never approached within sight of—the issue, by relying on the natural plants of their permanent pastures which virtually managed themselves. The difference in outlook was provoked by the pastoral prophets, from Elliott to Sir George Stapledon, who stirred the enthusiasm of the British farmer, while the Continental remained beyond the boundaries of grassland missionary endeavour.

An equal reason for the disparity was the greater readiness of the Briton to use the new fertilizers as they emerged from laboratory and factory. The 'natural' manures, either the excrement of farm livestock or the dung trampled into straw in the cattle yard and then 'made' in the heap, had long been supplemented by useful and useless expedients. Turf was stripped off before ploughing and slowly burnt—or 'denshired'—to release the soluble potashes; shoddy, or waste cloths and fibres of vegetable or animal origin, was spread and ploughed into market-garden land to hold moisture for the use of the plants and to decompose slowly into nutrients; night-soil, or refuse of the urban privies, was shipped by barge from London to the barley lands of north Hertfordshire; soot was treasured for its readily available nitrogen—the list of substitute manures seemed to be endless. None of them, however, was a purpose-made, commercially produced fertilizer. When such arrived, a revolution in agricultural productivity arrived too. For the first time the plant in the field could be given all the nutrients it needed for full growth. When, in a later period, irrigation became common the ideal environment for plant growth could be provided; and only the hazards of inclement weather and attack by disease or pest remained. Now that infection and infestation can be prevented or removed, only the weather is beyond the control of the farmer.

All this, in the mid-nineteenth century, was many decades ahead; but the 'artificial' fertilizers or 'bag manures'—as they were called, with some connotation of scorn, puzzlement or fear—were a major step towards the agricultural millennium. The first substitutes for the ancient farmyard manure were nearly as strange as the old ones. From about 1840 guano was shipped into Western Europe in great quantities from the south Pacific islands where thousands of generations of birds had left great deposits of their droppings. These were excavated, transhipped and delivered to the farmer who learnt the value of both the high nitrogen content of the pure bird dung and the usefulness of the bags in which it came. Other strange sources of fertility were the charnel houses and the communal graves of the battlefields, whence bones were carted, first to be roughly broken and left on the surface of fields to decompose into phosphates, and then to be dissolved in sulphuric acid in John Bennett Lawes's new factory for the manufacture of more readily available superphosphates. Gradually natural sources of the three primary plant nutrients—nitrogen, phosphate and potash —were discovered and exploited: the atmosphere itself for nitrogen or manufactured ammonias; coprolite beds for phosphates, and particularly the rock phosphate deposits of French North Africa; and potash from German deposits which began to be worked in the 1850s. By about 1870, the full range of 'artificials' was readily available to the high arable farmers; and such agricultural chemists as Liebig in Germany, Gilbert at Rothamsted research station in Hertfordshire, Anderson at Edinburgh, and Voelcker at the Royal Agricultural College at Cirencester were analysing the nutrient requirement of crops and freely distributing advice on how they should be provided, in theory.

Unfortunately for European agriculture there were two impediments to the full use of the new knowledge and the new materials. First, the collapse of European arable farming followed immediately upon the arrival of the full range of bag fertilizers, and to most cereal growers it seemed suicidal to invest in artificial manures for crops which would probably be sold at a loss—for only a handful of farmers realized that the additional yield from properly fed crops could turn a loss into a profit. And secondly, theory proved an incomplete adviser on plant nutrition: field trials with varying applications of fertilizers were only gradually found to be more useful in showing just how much manure could profitably be used, and such trials were few, improperly controlled, and immeasurably suspect to the great body of traditionally-minded arable men. It is little exaggeration to say that it took nearly a century after 1850 for fertilizers to come into full and profitable use in Britain, a little shorter time

in Holland and Denmark, and in France and Germany the millennium of the bag manure has yet to arrive.

The final tools to the hand of the farmer in this period were
mechanical implements and mechanical traction. In the past
the implements of agriculture had been solid and internally im-
mobile, becoming stronger and lighter as new materials replaced
the heavy timber of the plough and the harrows. The engineers
of the nineteenth century applied their mechanics to the tasks
of replacing with the movements of a machine the work hitherto
done laboriously by hand. The scythe gave way to the reciprocating knife in the cutter bar of the mower, which replicated
a score or more times the action of hand shears; the reaper cut
the corn and laid it conveniently in windrows, and soon a
knotting mechanism made it possible for the 'self-binder' to
reap and tie the standing corn into sheaves, which hitherto had
been collected and bound with straw ties by a score of women.
After a century of trials and errors, the familiar winter-long
sound of men wielding flails to thresh the ears of grain out to
the sheaves laid on the barn floor was heard no more: in its
place were the whir and bustle of the threshing drum, with one
man cutting the twine bands of the sheaves, a second feeding
them between the drum and the beaters which separated the
grain out of the ears, and a small army of other men sacking
off the threshed grain, dealing with the flights, awns or cavings
of the husks of the threshed ears, and forking the straw off the
straw walkers on to the elevator which took it up on to the
stack. The whole was driven by one of the new steam engines,
fed grimly with 'steam coal', which also moved the cavalcade of
threshing machine, elevator and living caravan along the un-
surfaced country lanes behind a man with a warning flag. Like
many other mechanical processes on the farm, the new way
required nearly as many men as the old way, but the work was
done more quickly, often better, and much less laboriously.
Likewise, elementary root harvesters appeared to replace—not
always efficiently—the men or women who had dug potatoes
by hand (where they were not ploughed out), or hand-pulled
beet; and rakes and tedders with moving parts did the work of

another army of women who had formerly turned and raked the hay field by hand. On the whole, the new methods simply copied the old hand movements, but performed them mechanically. Many of the most fundamental developments in farm mechanization awaited the inventive genius of the mid-twentieth century.

The second major advance was the coming of mechanical traction to replace—but very gradually—the heavy horse, which itself had taken over only recently from the plough ox. Development in every facet of mechanization was a slow process of the accretion of ideas, experiences, borrowings from other spheres of engineering; the pursuit of notions up blind alleys; the discarding of designs that looked practicable in the workshop but failed in practice in the field. The thresher had its origins in the early years of the eighteenth century; and it took more than a hundred years to come to full development. In the same way, as Harold Bennett has recently shown in his *Saga of the Steam Plough*, a Fire Engine (i.e. a steam engine) for Ploughing was patented in 1767; one that worked was made in 1833 by Josiah Parkes, the drainer, and John Heathcote, the Tiverton lace worker and great-grandfather of a future Minister of Agriculture; but it was not until John Fowler gathered the manifold ideas of scattered pioneers, interested Ransomes the plough manufacturers, and in April 1856 set a steam ploughing tackle to work at Nacton, Essex, that the concept arrived in a form in which suspicious and traditional arable farmers began to take an interest. Eighty-nine years had passed between first patent and first successful field use. The ordinary farmer felt no urgency to become mechanical in his operations; it was the odd men who pursued ideas slowly into practice. Even in 1856 the steam engine was drawn by horses; it was two years later that Fowler's engineers designed a self-mobile engine, but even this had to be steered by a horse in the shafts in front. By 1863 the new Fowler works at Leeds were turning out steam ploughing tackle as the world was to know it for about another century: the traction engine with endless wire ropes pulling a heavy plough body backwards and forwards across a field. The system had a vogue until, in the 1930s, the tractor took over; it continued in use on heavy soils for another twenty years; and the last steam ploughing contractor ceased business in the 1950s. The 'steamer' heralded the end of the farm horse as the common beast of traction, but it never came into sufficiently wide use actually to cause its disappearance from the shafts of plough and cart, for steam ploughing was used mainly for the quick cultivation of heavy wet land on large farms, or where deep ploughing to break up plough pan was needed. The plough team of horses continued to be the horseman's pride through the First World War, despite the competition of the first American Ford tractors, and into the inter-war years, to be discarded only when the urgencies of the Second World War made the tractor virtually the only motive force on the farm. Now, even the art of horse ploughing is lost; and horse classes at most British ploughing matches are discontinued.

The internal combustion-engined tractor had a similarly protracted and equally tortuous birth. The petroleum engine first impinged on agriculture at the Newcastle Royal Show of 1880; and, as Sir James Scott Watson and Mrs Hobbs wrote, it was soon installed as a stationary engine for threshing and milling so that 'it was no longer necessary to rise at four o'clock on threshing mornings to get the steam up for a start at seven'. During the next decade it became mobile, on wheels. In 1889 the American Burger steam traction engine was fitted with an oil engine. And in 1897 a Saunderson single-cylinder tractor made in Bedford was seen ploughing. The invention made little or no impact, and even as late as 1910 British, Continental and American tractors at the Royal Agricultural Society's third tractor trials at Baldock had more of a novelty than a practical value. The ploughing-up campaign in the First World War caused a number of American-built Fordsons to be imported, but they were unreliable in mechanical hands not yet accustomed to regular maintenance and the vagaries of an elementary ignition system and were discarded by most users with a sigh of relief well before the collapse of cereal growing after the repeal of the Corn Production Act of 1920. In 1931, when most middle-class families had a motor car, there was still fewer than one in twenty farms that had a tractor. This prime mover, an essential element in farming today, had been a long time a'coming. It was a dimly heard passing bell for the old agriculture, which took an even more unconscionable time a'dying; but during the interval between the two World Wars the causes of mortality for the old rural society were all assembled.

CHAPTER NINE

The Modern Scene

In those countries in Western Europe where industry has invaded the countryside and agriculture itself has become industrialized, there has been a sharper break with the habits of the past, a greater reorientation of mental outlook, a more complete change in the rural scene than at any time before. Whether this has been good or bad is a matter for personal judgment—much has been lost, and much gained—but of the suddenness of the transition, historically speaking, there can be no dispute. The reason for it is that agriculture has become completely commercial. On the farmer himself the impact of the business of farming, as distinct from the art of farming or—as it was often described—farming as a way of life, has caused a fundamental change. The Victorian husbandman was a great independent, a traditionalist, sufficient unto himself, uncooperative and narrow in his commerce. The farmer of the mid-nineteen sixties has surrendered the independence of commercial action to the numerous bodies who supply him with the raw materials of his trade, market his produce, speak for him politically and negotiate his prices. He has thrown tradition to the winds. First necessity and then fashion have led him to cooperate with his neighbours in many things, from the ownership of machinery to the purchase of yard brooms. He has a university degree or college diploma; he holidays in Majorca or Greece, and confers in New York or Copenhagen; he drives the most expensive motor car his income tax inspector will allow him to depreciate in his accounts; he appears on television. He has become indistinguishable from any other managing director of a sizeable company, for he has an invested capital as large as that of many a small factory—sometimes very much larger: a man whom his bank manager cannot afford not to finance to the limit of his credit-worthiness, and beyond.

The changes from the naïveties of the parish pump to the sophistication of cosmopolis have rubbed off on his younger farm staff. While the older men still tend to follow the old habits, the younger men are specialist technicians, a tractor driver and mechanic, a cow-milker of great virtuosity, a skilled pigman or poultryman, with an alertness, intelligence and sense of responsibility exceeding that of wage-earners in any other industry.

The rapid and complete alteration in the mental outlook of farmer and worker is a product of recent history. Rural events in all countries in Western Europe had moved in a steady procession through the mercantile changes of the late nineteenth century, the slow recovery from slump in the first decade and a half of the twentieth century, the brief impact of the First World War, and the long post-war depression. The transition was gradual: to the visitor from 1890, the countryside of 1930 would not have seemed wholly unfamiliar. Bungalows were springing up in the lanes, but horses still pulled the ploughs; every cottage had its wireless aerial, but the children who lived in it still went to the village school; roads were metalled and becoming busy with motor cars, but Shorthorn cows grazed fields that were still as the enclosures had left them, and hens scratched in the farmyard; farm labourers wore boots bought not from the local cobbler but at a multiple store, but two farmers out of three still went to corn exchange or cattle market every week. In the remoter parts—in the Welsh hills, the Alpine valleys, on the small Breton holdings time continued to stand still.

The latest agricultural revolution, which began as recently as the 1940s, has wrought more change in twenty-five years than occurred in two centuries in mediaeval times. At the root of it have been two major factors: the growing impact of international economics and politics, and technical invention. The countries of Western Europe stimulated their agricultures into unprecedented productivity towards the close of the First World War, to make good the shortages caused by blockade. The unnaturally high level of the output and the policy of food production at any price made post-war European farming particularly vulnerable to the two inevitable sequels to the war: a return of normal overseas supplies, and depression and a sharp fall in purchasing power when the artificial and controlled economy of war-time ran down and an unplanned economy resumed its sway. The agricultural slump of the 1920s was profound and widespread, and as devastating in its effects as the depression in the cereal market of the 1880s and 1890s had been. The response of most European farmers was, however, diametrically opposite to that of the late nineteenth century. As the price for a ton of wheat fell—from the already low level of 1927 it slumped to half in the international depression of 1930 and 1931—the farmer sought to maintain his income by producing more, so that the Western European production of thirty-two million tons in 1921 became one of nearly forty-eight million tons by 1938. As a result, tariff barriers, pulled down during the war, were built again, even in countries where the *laissez faire* of free trade had been the national policy for many generations.

Britain herself, with her long tradition of non-interference with international commerce, was the last and the most reluctant builder of a tariff barrier. The war-time guaranteed prices for cereals were abandoned suddenly in 1921, to the consternation of farmers who had been given firm political assurances that they would be maintained for several years at least. Successive governments persisted in an open-market policy, allowing nearly free entry to a flood of American grains, New Zealand and Argentine meat, Danish eggs and bacon. At first a subsidy on sugar-beet was the only aid offered, and it was taken up so widely that the acreage of sugar-beet increased twentyfold in ten years. Only in the extremity of agricultural depression did governments from 1931 onwards begin to apply tariffs to imported foodstuffs, but even then they so weakened them by Imperial preferences that they were not fully effective. In 1932 a Wheat Act introduced guaranteed prices, and a deficiency payment made good the difference between guaranteed and market price. At times this rose to nearly fifty per cent. Friendly critics of British farming objected that this subsidy perpetuated the old fallacy, that wheat was the cornerstone of agriculture. It was the argument of the fourteenth, sixteenth and late nineteenth century all over again. The critics, led by Astor and Rowntree, denied that bread remained the staff of life or that Britain was the natural place in which to grow British wheat. For other commodities marketing boards were set up, first and most successfully for milk; and some unsuccessful attempts were made to stabilize the bacon market by voluntary restriction of imports.

Against this slight and hesitant return to the protectionism of the Corn Laws political economists resurrected all the arguments in favour of free trade; that both the countryside and the nation as a whole were best served by maintaining fewer but better-paid people at work on really viable farms and by building up Britain's industrial strength by the unrestricted import of food in payment for exported goods. But acute distress of the farming community and the moral obligation on Government to relieve that distress—which an influential but not yet powerful National Farmers' Union constantly emphasized—gradually strengthened the policy of agricultural support, with the result that when preparations were made for the Second World War by the emergency measures of 1938 the price indices for farm produce had regained about half the ground lost since the 1930–31 depression and there had been an increase of fifty per cent in the wheat acreage and a quarter of a million in the number of cows. The measures to secure Imperial preference had also worked so effectively that food imports from the Empire had risen by forty-three per cent and those from foreign countries had fallen by seventeen per cent.

The responses of the other European countries to the economic challenges of the inter-war years was very different. France used import quotas with considerable success, and at a cost far less than that of tariffs which French statesmen regarded as useless instruments in an international market of such unprecedented instability. In the years immediately before the Second World War France also set about what M. Nogaro called 'the organization of markets'. This included the sale of wine only against permits and the virtual nationalization of trade in wheat, and it proved so effective that the prices of French farm produce were virtually insulated against and detached from all influence by the international markets for foodstuffs. That the French

farmer achieved this level of stability in an economically un-
predictable world and amidst all his instabilities of government
was largely due to the pressures exerted by the agricultural
syndicates, chambers and unions which proliferated in the 1930s
and significantly influenced the very large rural vote.

Germany, of course, had become the prime example of an
organized society in which the health of the agricultural industry
took second place only to military strength. As soon as she
regained control of her affairs after the First World War,
Germany returned to tariff protection; but this was not sufficient to shield her farmers from the world depression of the
early 1930s. These men who faced the ruin of their rural enter-
prises were among the readiest sections of the nation to take
National Socialism to their hearts, particularly as it offered a
coherent policy for agriculture as one of its main aims. The
author of the Nazi farm policy was Walther Darré, who when
he became Hitler's Minister of Agriculture in 1933, brought the
nation's farming into the Party organization by placing it under
the control of his State Food Corporation (Reichsnährstand),
compelling everyone concerned with agriculture to belong to it,
organizing all marketing through it, and determining most commodity prices within narrow limits. Within a year this Corporation had become Hitler's instrument for bringing his policy for
increasing home food production as near to self-sufficiency as
possible; and as he absorbed his neighbours he brought them
also under its control. Before the outbreak of war in 1939 the
Reichsnährstand had become to German farmers virtually what
Stalin's chain of control of his collectives had become to Russia,
except that the organization of German farming stopped short
of collectivization. The policy worked well for both partners.
By 1936 the Nazi government had reduced food imports to
nearly half the pre-depression figure; and the farmer was receiving nearly a third more for his produce than he had done
before the Nazis came into power. To as industrial a country
as Germany such a policy of agricultural self-sufficiency would
have been disastrous in normal times. But to a nation girding
its loins for war it was an essential major line of internal defence.
And to the farming industry it brought rationalization, an

unprecedented stability, and a sense of urgency that British agriculture was not to develop until the Second World War was well under way; and was not fully to achieve until the Agriculture Act of 1947.

True, the British Government laid down precise plans in advance. This was one lesson remembered from the First World War, when the submarine blockade of 1917 caught both government and farming unprepared. A chain of requisition from Ministry of Food through Ministry of Agriculture to county war agricultural executive committees was forged; and the county committees directed not only the broad lines of production but also often the fields that had to be sown to a particular crop, for which both a market and a price were guaranteed. Livestock suffered, as much from the ploughing up of pasture as from the rationing of feeding-stuffs in order that grain might be consumed at first hand by the nation, rather than second hand by processing into meat. In gross figures, food imports were halved; the arable acreage in Britain was raised from twelve to eighteen million; and a new generation of British farmers had a taste of a security and prosperity that had not been known in agriculture since their fathers had enjoyed the nation's solicitude from 1917 to 1920.

Across the English Channel, French farmers were receiving the attention of government, but on behalf of the occupying power through a counterpart of the Reichsnährstand, the Corporation Paysanne. For half a century France had followed, but a long way behind, the progress towards industrialization of her neighbours England and Germany. Hitler reversed the trend, and set the Vichy Government the task of restoring France to an agricultural economy on largely peasant lines; but both the tools and the cash for rural redevelopment were denied and French farmers emerged from the war in 1945 somewhat worse off in terms both of money and productive capacity than when they had entered it. Both Holland and Denmark suffered similarly under occupation, the Low Countries being devastated by the fighting and Denmark suffering the disappearance of both her sources of supply of her essential imported feeding-stuffs and her great traditional market, Britain. Alone in Western

Europe, the Professional Neutral—Switzerland—pursued an un-
eventful and prosperous course, with her small farms gradually
disappearing in amalgamations into larger units and an accelerat-
ing movement of peasants' sons into industry. Between 1940
and 1950 the agricultural working population fell from 380,000
to 327,000. In their own small ways, the remaining Swiss
farmers grew in acres and in prosperity as the conflict was waged
around them—exhibiting once again the rewards of profoundly
wise policies of territorial unambition and minding their own
business.

Apart from Switzerland, therefore, the countries of Western
Europe entered the peace in 1945 with agricultural problems
of great magnitude on their hands: France with a depressed
industry, the Low Countries and Denmark with several years'
disruption of their normal production for export and the Low
Countries with much devastation to make good, the new Federal
Republic of Western Germany divorced from the fertile corn-
lands now in the Soviet sector and with only poor farming
country left to her, and Britain with her half-million farmers
determined not to lose their new-found prosperity and security.
The answer chosen by each country has in the past two decades
done more than to attempt to satisfy the reasonable ambitions
of its farmers: it has set a course for the whole of its rural
evolution. Probably never before has so much been changed in
the countryside in so short a period as a result of the deliberate
choice by governments of agricultural policies. The policies
introduced by the Labour Government in Britain in the Agriculture Act of 1947 have proved so far to be the most successful
from most, but not all, points of view. The Act guaranteed
markets and prices for 'such part of the nation's food and other
agricultural produce as in the national interest it is desirable to
produce in the United Kingdom'. The loophole for future default
was a large one, but to date successive governments have played
fairly enough with the spirit of the Act; and disputes between
the Ministry of Agriculture and the Exchequer on the one side,
and the National Farmers' Unions of the U.K., now very powerful in the lobby and in the marginal constituencies, on the other
have been merely a matter of degree of emphasis. To implement

the declaration in the Act, prices for most commodities have been decided at an annual Price Review: and the guarantee of return and market made good by the deficiency payments system, a device peculiar to Britain. On a free market, open also to imported produce under a fairly complete return to free trade, the price received by the farmer has been made up to the guaranteed figure, for a standard quantity of quite generous dimensions, by the payment to him by the State of the deficit. This method has served three purposes: to give the farmer an assured return, adjusted to rising (or falling) costs of production; to allow unrestricted imports of food to continue; and to maintain shop prices at a reasonable level. It has had two drawbacks: the consumer has levelled the taunt against the farmer of having his inefficiency subsidized, whereas in fact it is often the price to the consumer that is subsidized, indirectly out of taxation; and secondly, on occasion heavy imports of food at low prices have raised the deficiency payments bill to an intolerable level. But this latter has been a small and infrequent price to pay for agricultural stability and prosperity, the results of which will be discussed soon.

Other, less unusual, devices have been used in the post-war years to assist the State in moving agriculture in the desired directions. The major tool of national policy has been the annual Price Review which by adjusting prices has kept supply and demand tolerably in step. But for some years it has been the declared intention of Government to enable the farmer to increase his 'efficiency' (an overworked but necessary omnibus word), so that subsidies on his produce can be gradually run down. To this end, grants have been given for farm buildings, small farm reorganization and amalgamation, pensions and quittance, on fertilizers and hill stock, on office records and drainage and roads, on beef-type calves and the ploughing up of old grass, and for a score of other tools of agricultural production. Over the twenty years from the end of the war to the time of writing two major steps forward have been taken, and a third is emerging. The first step was to continue the war-time policy of food at any price, to ensure that the people of Britain were fed. The second, when world food supplies increased, was to encourage the farmer towards lower production costs, so that he could become competitive with imported produce. The third is to convert the traditional way of living—an offspring of the ancient subsistence farming by country gentlemen—into a normal commercial business, to which all the criteria of commerce in returns on capital, on labour, and on the use of national assets can be applied; and this is in order that British farming may fit naturally into an economy based on well-balanced import-export figures.

Here, as in most of Western Europe, such success as has been achieved in modernizing the structure of agriculture has come from the fact that national farm policies have been generally agreed by all political parties and therefore taken outside party politics. In France, Mr Tracy has written, the importance of agriculture has been recognized almost without question 'and the rest of the community seems to accept an obligation to preserve a large and reasonably prosperous agriculture'. To do this, the French post-war governments reverted to the pre-war policy of insulating their farmers from world competition by import control, either under licence or through state-controlled agencies. As early as 1950 domestic surpluses arose, and a vigorous food export policy was pursued under the Marshall Plan, to help to close the gap in the national balance of payments. This caused on occasion some embarrassment to her neighbours when French cereals flooded into their ports at artificially low export-subsidized prices. In about 1961, both surpluses and the cost of the highly complex price support system looked like getting out of hand, and a fund for the improvement of farm 'structure' (the jargon for the range of farm sizes, not the buildings of a holding) was established with the same objective as the British amalgamation plan of 1965—to bribe or pension small farmers into retirement or other jobs—and also to encourage commodity sales through organizations similar to the successful marketing boards in Britain. In the first year, according to a statement made to me by M. Pisani, the Minister of Agriculture, 100,000 French peasants left their holdings. The policy has aroused misgivings among older Frenchmen, who still look to a numerous peasantry as a staple source of national strength; and their traditional views have found mouthpieces in the several disunited farmers' organizations. That it was forced through was a mark of the power of the new Confédération Générale de l'Agriculture, the national body of young farmers which has rejuvenated French agricultural thought, both in policy and in technique. In particular they have taken a longer view in technical and structural advances than has the previous generation, which has sought to preserve a large peasant element in French national farming because the complementary high level of price support has kept prices, and therefore affluence, up on the larger farms to an even greater degree. The same kind of unenlightened self-interest has, perhaps, not been wholly absent from the concern of British farmers' unions for their smaller members.

France has now (1965) turned her export eye upon her companions in the Common Market—the European Economic Community—and in particular upon her neighbour, the West German Federal Republic. One of the first actions of the new Federal Republic after the war was the creation of the bodies which have been its instruments of agricultural control ever since, the Import and Storage Boards for the main commodities. Like France, Germany has tried to insulate its farmers from fluctuations in world markets and from international surpluses and shortages, and a major element in its policy has been to bring farmers' incomes up as close as possible to the high standard of its booming industries. The Boards—Einfuhr und Vorratsstellen—have been in effect adjustment agents between home supplies and imports, controlling the price of a commodity to the importer, dictating its marketing and stockpiling, and even vetoing its entry. The system of import intervention has been reinforced by fairly complete control of home supplies. To the consumer, this method of stabilizing supplies has kept up the retail price without the help of subsidies, thus making the housewife pay for rural prosperity direct and not indirectly through taxation. To the importer, and to the overseas supplier, it has built up an arbitrary wall which has disturbed international trade unduly. And the annual cost has been high —currently about £8 per head of the population of the Republic, equal to the French national farm support bill and higher than Britain's.

Along with the levelling out of supplies through the commodity boards, the Federal Republic has also indulged in extensive and expensive reform of the structure of holdings. Its problem here was probably greater than that of any other country in the whole of Europe except Italy and the Soviet Union, for its largest and most economically sound farms were lost in the Soviet sector, and Western Germany was left with some intolerably fragmented holdings. A typical problem was that in the Eifel uplands on the western border which I examined in 1961. Here, the farmhouses and steadings were crowded in the villages, and the land was scattered in acre fields over several square miles. Now, a new house and buildings have been erected by the Federal Government in the centre of each consolidated farm. The cost is met half by State grant and half by loan repayable at $1\frac{1}{2}$ per cent interest over sixty years. In this cost is included every piece of labour-saving equipment that can be justified on sixty acres. In 1962, expenditure on consolidation of holdings was of the order of 3,000 million Deutschmarks (nearly £250 million), and the economy in production costs in return for the steadily rising consolidation bill since then has not yet been apparent. Indeed, the criticism is that the attempt by France, Germany and Italy to accelerate the normal processes of peasant decay by such humanitarian means as pensions, departure payments and subsidized unification of scattered holdings has been ill-conceived; but to let natural decay take its course would have been socially impossible and an open invitation to political unrest. It has been this closely-guarded West German citadel of a high-cost, high-price economy, with its very high level of imported foodstuffs and with cereal prices running at nearly double the world level, that the Common Market has threatened to lay wide open to the free movement of French cereals produced at a far lower cost.

Elsewhere in Western Europe, the post-war superstructure of agricultural control has been less intricate and less complete than in the three principal nations of Britain, France and Western Germany. Switzerland has relied mainly on import-export agreements to maintain a high level of protection for her farming. Denmark, with her highly vulnerable export trade in pig and dairy products, first used with much success such modern techniques of salesmanship as brand marks, jealously guarded levels of quality, and attractive packing; and only when her traditional markets began to close against her did she resort, in 1961, to direct subsidies to her farmers. And in Holland a vigorous policy of support for agriculture—which provides eleven per cent of national production—is pursued. Import levies on cereals, sugar and meat are supplemented by deficiency payments for milk of such a size that they supply the average farmer's net profit, and by State purchase and stockpiling of surplus products. Her most efficient horticulture virtually protects itself by co-operation at every stage through to the fraud-proof clock auction and an international market intelligence system at a level matched only by that of Italian horticulture.

It was upon this bewildering chaos of agricultural policies that the concept of the European Economic Community (the Common Market, or the Six) arrived in 1957. Because this concept is not yet certain of survival, no more can be said here than that it envisages the creation first of an economically united bloc of West European nations with all barriers to internal trade removed and common levels of costs and prices fixed for all; and ultimately of a political bloc into which national sovereignties would be sunk. The agricultural and social implications of the Community are profound: for France, an open market in industrial West Germany at prices above her present level; for Germany, the prospect of a flood of food imports at prices well below her own artificially maintained returns to her farmers; for Holland, the curtailment of the imports of cheap transatlantic feeding grains upon which much of her pre-eminent milk production is based; for Denmark—not a member —the closing of her European markets by a tariff wall around the Common Market countries; and for Britain—whose application for membership was vetoed by France—nearly every possible economic advantage except in the sphere of horticulture, but a possible loss of the treasured deficiency payment system of agricultural support.

If the European Economic Community came into full existence it would complicate still further the present complexities of political manipulation of agricultural production: and the major decisions affecting farming would be taken internationally in Brussels. This is a measure of the distance that the simple arts of food production have travelled in less than a century, since the nations of Europe first had serious occasion to seek to control the free movement of foodstuffs in an attempt to stem the flood of American grain. In these eighty years the repercussions of these economic expedients have been added to the effects of industrial and technological developments and of new social thinking to change the country people and the countryside of Britain especially, and to a lesser degree of all Western Europe, with unprecedented speed. A village and its community in, say, the English Midlands is so utterly unlike the village and the community of a century ago that the villager of the 1860s could never have foreseen its present aspect—whereas the parish of the 1760s would have seemed to them not so very old-fashioned or strange.

Part of the change has come, only recently, from the new techniques of agriculture. These have evolved very fast in Britain since the Second World War, mainly through the work of a few scores of farmers using new tools and new fundamental knowledge which have emerged from the network of research stations and experimental farms maintained both by commercial firms and the Agricultural Research Council. That these techniques have spread so rapidly from the pioneers to the main army of farmers is a reflection of the effectiveness of the channels of information. The establishment of the National Agricultural Advisory Service in England and Wales at the end of the war, which put technically qualified officers at the beck and call of all farmers thirsty for advice, and a network of specialists on tap behind them; a technical Press unequalled in usefulness throughout the world, and perhaps also in any industry; a plethora of demonstrations, conferences, shows; a chain of agricultural education from university level down to day release courses: all these have made the acquisition of knowledge, first of techniques and latterly of business management, painlessly easy.

To an uninformed eye at a train window, the arrival of new methods may not be very evident: the green wheat springing in the drills, the yellow drooping barley-heads waiting for the cutterbar look much as they have always done, but radically new methods have gone to the painting of the arable picture. Even the plough, the oldest of all the tools of farming except perhaps the sickle, is beginning to give way to the chemical destruction of the surface vegetation by one of the complete, short-lived weedicides that leave a clean ground for shallow cultivation and drilling. The much debated rotation has nearly disappeared too. With selective weedicides cereal crops can be kept clean; with fertilizers fertility can be maintained; and cereal crops can be grown year after year on the same field so that the arable farm can move a long way towards monoculture—at least until one of the factors gives way and infestation with soil pests or infection with fungoid or virus diseases builds up, or soil structure and fertility demand a rest. On suitable soil, in wise hands, the limits of monoculture are not in sight; for nearly all Western Europe is free from the factors which have devastated with soil erosion the original home of one-crop farming, the United States of America. These new techniques are also aided by the breeding of new cereal varieties, particularly in France and the Scandinavian countries and Russia, which are specifically designed to resist the infections and infestations of continuous cropping, to respond to heavy applications of fertilizers, and to ripen in succession so that they come ready to the combine one after another.

The combine itself has probably done more than any single development in farming to change the shape of rural life. Even the 'self-binder', which grew out of the early-Victorian reaper, needed a small army of men or women to put up the sheaves into stooks, to fork them up on to the wagon, to stack them, and to thresh them out of the stack during the winter. The combined harvester—its full name before it became abbreviated—is what it says it is: it combines in one machine the reaper and the threshing drum. A modern (1965) combine working in good conditions can harvest two or three acres an hour, and deliver three to six tons of threshed grain into a trailer for delivery to store or drier. The harvest team need consist of no more than three men for cutting, carting, drying and delivering into store: in the pre-combine days the manhours needed for three acres would have been sixty-five, not three. The peak labour force has therefore been decreased more than twentyfold, and along with the mechanization of other farm operations this has been responsible for what is wrongly termed the drift from the land, for the accompanying release of country cottages from farm to other uses, and for the radical change in the mental and social complexion of the English village.

This is rather running ahead of the theme. The 'complete harvester' for the other time-consuming crops, notably potatoes, hops and sugar-beet in Britain and maize in France, has replaced another army, that of the potato and hop pickers and the sugar-beet team. Where men once threshed corn by flail on the barn floor, or fed the threshing drum, the only mid-winter work remaining on the farm is the potato sorting, which has not yet succumbed to mechanization; although the crop is now sorted in comfort out of the indoor potato store and not in the acute discomfort of a clamp open to the English weather at its worst. As a result, the rheumatic, bowed and thirsty farm labourer has gone, and in his place is a normal man.

And if the man has been bettered in his condition, so has the animal—although the critics of rural change who lament the passing of the crusted characters also deplore the disappearance of livestock into what they call factory farms. The basic reasons for what are more properly called intensive livestock farms are three: land is now too costly, to rent or to buy, for it to be misused as a winter exercise ground—which is what it virtually was for the out-wintered herd or flock; stock thrive when they are sheltered from the worst of the weather, and do not have to use most of their food merely to produce heat in order to keep themselves alive; and a far closer control over every aspect of livestock husbandry can be exercised over a housed animal than a ranched one—in health, feeding, growth rate and breeding. In return for this precision, animals capable of a high performance are given an opportunity to reach towards their maximum potential output of meat, milk, eggs or wool.

The development of intensive methods of livestock management has, therefore, been accompanied by the breeding of more efficient stock. In beef production the association has been particularly marked. In lowland Britain the outwintered bullock has nearly disappeared, and has been replaced by either 'barley beef' housed for the whole of its short life of about a year, or by 'eighteen-month-old beef' in which a summer at grass intervenes between two winters of indoor feeding. Both systems make use of the new techniques of feeding barley which has been stored wet from the harvest in a sealed tower silo in which it is preserved by its own gases, and from which it is delivered mechanically into the manger. The system originated in America with store-sealed maize; and in southern Europe, and particularly the fertile maize-growing area of the Po Valley in Italy, it is copied in its entirety, even to the extent of flying in surplus American calves for feeding. In the areas of skilful pastoral management, which are confined to southern Britain and Holland, grass cut at a short and nutritious stage is substituted for barley and fed as high dry matter silage from which very few of the proteins and carbohydrates of the original grasses have been lost. In such intensive beef production, stock is housed and fed to perfection, and although flavour in the meat is sacrificed for early maturity and slaughter, in every respect the system is the very antithesis of the cruelty of 'factory production' with which its critics charge it.

Similar methods for feeding and housing have been developed for the dairy herd, again particularly in Britain and Holland and to some little extent on the newly made small farms of the West German Federal Republic and on some co-operative dairy farms of suburban France. To these are added, at the one end, various precisely controlled systems of grazing the highly productive strains of grasses, bred particularly at the Welsh Plant Breeding Station at Aberystwyth—the S strains—and fertilized to the limit of their response; and at the other end, labour-saving milking 'parlours' which strive for the highest output of milk per manhour to the limit of—and occasionally beyond—good stock husbandry. The resulting combination of loose-housing (the jargon for keeping cows untethered in a covered yard); self-feeding of silage by the herd; milking by one man in the parlour, with the milk from the forty cows milked each hour piped to a refrigerated bulk storage tank which has replaced the familiar churn; and mechanized disposal of the effluent: all these have transformed dairy farming completely from its condition of only a decade ago, when hand-milking in the traditional cowshed where the cows were tied all winter by their necks was still the common method. Such devices as slatted floors for the dung and urine to fall through, individual foul-proof cubicles for the cows, and automatic feeding of concentrated foods by the pull of a handle are taken into use yearly.

The pig also has been moved out of its traditional sty into one of two extreme types of housing. The controlled environment house, with exactly adjusted temperature and rate of air change, provides the optimum condition for growth of the weaned pig into porker or baconer and the greatest economy in food; the field house for sows and litters gives the healthiest possible conditions for young stock during the most critical period. Even the sheep, most natural of all domesticated live-stock, tends to be wintered indoors, both to prevent damage to sodden pastures and to make the job of the shepherd more comfortable. The concept of sheephousing is of great antiquity. It was common practice in England with the mediaeval flocks of fine-woolled sheep, hence the numerous 'sheepcotes' in place-names; and, indeed, in most well-managed manorial and monastic flocks. Although it continued in use particularly in France up to the present day, it became uncommon but never unknown in Britain for five hundred years or more, and its recent revival is the result of increasing the number of sheep carried to the acre to the point where wintering out of doors is impracticable. The system is seen to perfection today in the Île de Paris, where specially built sheephouses of advanced design accommodate the Merino-cross flocks whose mid-winter lambs are reared and finished inside in the greatest comfort for man and beast.

Such intensive methods of livestock management require three things: stock of high performance, nicely balanced feeding, and great attention to the prevention and treatment of disease. In all three the scientist has brought to the aid of the farmer new applications of genetic theory, new developments in the science of animal nutrition, and new drugs undreamt of a generation or even a decade or two ago. The first, genetic improvement, is based on the measurement of the performance of the progeny of individual parents so that the most successful sires and dams can be selected. The progress that has been made is mathematical rather than fundamentally genetic. Robert Bakewell, nearly two hundred years ago, proved his rams by hiring them out so that they should be widely used upon as random a sample of ewes as possible; and he then assessed their worth by the stock they got. The scientific breeder of today has not progressed very much. The mechanism of inheritance is better understood, but it can by no means be controlled so that the geneticist can say that by mating A to B the offspring will inherit these characteristics from this parent in that degree. At best, he can apply the law of averages over a fairly large number of progeny. The advances that have been made are the testing of sires on a far greater number of dams than Bakewell could ever have used: the use of artificial insemination—developed at Cambridge in the 1930s for cattle, by the Pig Industry Development Association in Britain in the past few years for pigs, and in Russia during the 1960s for sheep—this use of A.I. enabled the semen from one bull to be used to inseminate 20,000 or 30,000 cows in one year. And the second advance on the Bakewell method is purely one of computation: punched card indices and electronic computers have removed all limit to the number of calculations that can be made from breeding records.

It is the application of this statistically sound method of genetic assessment that has led to such progress as has been made in livestock breeding for performance. The first widespread use of performance recording was for dairy cows. In the 1890s the Duke of Westminster's Dairy Shorthorn herds and some other herds were having their milk yields recorded daily in England, and in Holland and Denmark milk recording was already fairly common. In 1963 twenty-four per cent of all dairy cows in England and Wales were recorded; in Holland about seventy per cent of cows are recorded; in Denmark nearly sixty per cent. Accurate records provide three main lines of information: the genetic potential of the dam, the ability of a bull to improve upon that potential in their offspring, and the day-to-day or week-by-week effect on the milk yield of the cow of changes in management—feed, environment and stress factors in particular. The cynic would say that the only progress that has been made is in the standard of livestock management, and that the genetic improvement that has been brought about is negligible; and it is not easy to refute him. More recently, British beef cattle breeders have introduced American methods of recording the growth rates of beef bulls and their offspring in an attempt to select out the best sires; but the results so far are not free from contradiction. In both beef and dairy cattle the emphasis has been upon selection within breeds, rather than the manufacture of new breeds along eighteenth- and nineteenth-century lines; the only exception is the experiments in West Germany and in Britain aimed at either making a new breed or breeding a supply of hybrids for commercial livestock men from the Friesian and Jersey stock, in order that the high yield of the Friesian and the high butterfat content of the Jersey may be combined.

Hybridization has revolutionized the modern poultry industry. Within a decade the familiar breeds have completely disappeared from the general and specialist farms, so that the once familiar Rhode Island Reds and White Leghorns are now nearly museum-pieces. The hybrid sheep has a longer history. Britain alone in Europe, probably in the world, is unique in not keeping her sheep breeds pure. Culley's Border Leicesters have been used for at least a century as crossing rams on Cheviot and other north country hill ewes to produce a hybrid dam—the Scottish Half-Bred—which is then mated to a Down ram to produce large numbers of lambs that grow and finish fast. More recently, the Border Leicester ram has been similarly used on the Welsh Mountain and the Romney Marsh ewe. The hybrid so manufactured is not self-perpetuating, and has to be remade from

LIFE FROM THE LAND

the parent stock for each new generation. The one new breed
of importance to emerge in recent decades among the larger
farm livestock has been a sheep, the Colbred. For this, Mr A. H.
Colburn brought East Friesland ewes from the Dutch-German
border to his Gloucestershire farm and after experimenting with
crosses of a number of British breeds finally evolved and fixed
a sheep which combined the very high fecundity and milking
ability of the East Friesland with the good meat conformation
of the British Down breeds. Some Finnish sheep have also
recently been imported into Britain for a similar experiment.
In both cases the main object has been to replace the prolificacy
and high milk yield which Bakewell and other improvers lost
in their pursuit of carcase size, fat and growth rate. The East
Friesland, Finnish and several other breeds in Europe and most
types of sheep in the Near and Middle East, never having
suffered improvement, have preserved these original faculties
intact.

The vigour and thriftiness of the hybrid, which are its particular virtues, are also beginning to be utilized 'scientifically' in
the pig. For half a century pig feeders have known of the value
of the hybrid Large White–Wessex piglet; and in New Zealand
Professor McMeekan has combined this with recorded performance to produce hybrids for breeding and feeding on commercial farms with great success. In the past year or two, some
of the large British bacon-curing firms have provided a similar
service to their feeders, manufacturing for them hybrid sows
from parents of high breeding ability. The short period between
generations and the large litters of the pig have enabled greater
basic genetic progress to be made than in any other farm livestock except poultry, which also have a rapid succession of
generations; and the official testing schemes for breeding stock
first in Denmark and then in Britain, West Germany and Holland have perfected methods of selecting boars and sows which
can give reasonably repeatable performance of the required
characteristics in their progeny. The period is one of transition
from the traditional bacon, or Wiltshire side, type of pig with
great length to provide plenty of rashers, only a thin covering
of fat on the back to keep them lean, and more weight in the

valuable hams than in the less valuable forequarters, to a heavier pig from which the particular sort of meat required can be cut out; and the characteristics which are needed are a matter for discussion. Because livestock breeders are men of fixed opinions —one hesitates to call them prejudices—the discussion is heated, interminable and inconclusive.

A comparison of production figures for England and Wales between 1936–37 and 1964–65 shows how successful the scientist and the farmer in combination have been. The following increases are due mainly to better feeding of stock and of crops (in the form of fertilizers) and partly to the use of better bred livestock and seed:

	1936–37	1964–65	
Wheat	17·8	33·0	cwt/acre
Barley	16·5	29·0	cwt/acre
Potatoes	6·6	8·9	tons/acre
Sugar-beet	1·2	2·2	tons sugar/acre
Milk	540	780	gallons/cow

Not the least important of the influences for change in agriculture is the fashion in diet, which has altered most in those countries which have most recently passed through the curtain of peasantry into the modern world. Frenchmen now eat, per head, only fifty-seven per cent of the bread and sixty-nine per cent of the potatoes they ate before the First War. For Germany the figures are seventy-three and seventy-six per cent. But consumption of sugar and cheese has nearly doubled. Frenchmen eat more than twice as much meat and Germans twice as much fish. In Britain consumption of sugar per head has risen forty-three per cent, of fats ninety-two, of eggs eighty-seven, of milk 216, and of fruit 129 per cent. Moreover, an increasing proportion of this food is now processed, pre-packed or even 'ovenready', so that standardization of quality and type of food becomes more important every year. This requires either large-scale production, often under the supervision of the buyers, or quality-controlled co-operative marketing. One of the largest supermarkets in Britain, with 250 stores, will buy only table

chickens of a few specified breeds which have been subject
neither to routine antibiotic treatment nor chemical pesticides,
and which can be on sale in the store, unfrozen, within twenty-
four hours of slaughter. This is a far cry from the barnyard
cockerel bought at the butcher's round the corner.

This revolution in the techniques of agriculture has affected
the countryside in proportion to the degree of change in farming methods. In places where livestock and arable husbandry
have pursued their ancient ways the alterations are scarcely
perceptible. Women still tend the cows on the Alpine pastures
underneath Dent Blanche as they have done for centuries; oxen
still plough the small Bavarian strips of arable; the remotest
Welsh mountain flocks are managed much as they were two
hundred—even five hundred—years ago. Here the contacts with
the new rural civilization grow slowly; the rural population
dwindles slowly; and the countryside away from the main roads
wears most of its ancient aspect. But where continuous corn-
growing or modern livestock production units proliferate both
country and countrymen have changed in an historical twinkling
of an eye. Other, equally fundamental, changes have also played
their parts: the increasing circumference of commuting around
cities, centralized education, new towns, above all the motor car.
But farming developments have run, quite independently, alongside these, and added their own touches to the evolving rural
picture of an industrialized countryside where a conscious effort
has to be made to preserve the last of the hallmarks of true
rurality.

Perhaps the most obvious of the outward and visible signs of
a mental and sociological revolution are country buildings. In
Britain—or at least lowland arable Britain—the farmstead
evolved slowly and logically. Upon enclosure, the farmhouses
and buildings were dispersed from the village into the centre of
the new nucleated holdings so that only here and there—
in contrast with much of Continental Europe—do the farm-
steadings still line the village street: some parishes in pastoral
Leicestershire remain as an exception. According to the date of
enclosure, the isolated steadings that besprinkle the countryside
at intervals of half a mile or so are of the great Tudor and early

Stuart rebuilding, less often eighteenth century, most frequently Victorian monuments of the great arable prosperity of the mid-nineteenth century. Rebuilding and new building then virtually ceased until recent, prosperous decades. Alongside this change, the farm buildings became separated in the sixteenth century from the ancient longhouse farm and gradually became specialist in their function. The practised eye can detect here and there, remaining from quite an early date, the stone-built sheephouses, the round buildings that housed the gear in which an orbiting horse worked a central drive, the covered bullock yards long since converted into machinery stores, the wooden granaries that once stood on staddles as protection against vermin but are now lowered to the ground and converted to garages. All these relics are fit subjects for study by the students of the new industrial archaeology before they are swept away, usually necessarily, to make place for multi-purpose umbrella structures in concrete. The aspect of the countryside changes as these old buildings in the materials that were derived from the land are demolished and new fabricated materials come in.

The change is not necessarily always for the worse. The alteration that is more debatable is that of user of the farm cottages. As the small peasant holdings disappeared, mainly in the period 1750–1850, their farmhouses became the homes of farm labourers who no longer lived in the farm servants' quarters of the farm in which they worked. The hired hands' cottages usually have no greater antiquity than this; and a large proportion of them date only from the mid-Victorian days of booming arable prosperity. Between that time and the advent of the 'council house' only a handful of model landlords kept workers' housing in step with the artisan dwelling standards in the towns, despite much state exhortation, some inspection and condemnation, and a little grant aid. This stagnation in housing was a contributory factor in the stagnation of the village, from which the old crafts and services had fled into the towns leaving behind only a one-class society, that of the farmers in their various degrees, below that of the gentry. Not until local authorities began to build houses in some numbers in the 1920s and farm workers moved into them in mass did a new element introduce itself into village society, that of the foreigners—the commuters, the weekenders and the retired professional people. They not only moved in mass into the countryside, they also moved in mass into the old smallholders' and workers' homes, which were transformed into 'country cottages'. This alien element, together with the rapid fall in the number of farm workers which mechanization and the better use of labour brought about, has altered the occupational balance of at least the British lowlands, and has left the farming community in a minority. In my own village, forty miles from London and not untypical of the East Anglian and Midland mixed farming belt of central England, there are only twenty men now directly engaged in the practice of agriculture out of a population of six hundred. The percentage of non-farming households dwindles to nearly nil in upland Wales and Scotland, in much of Eire and rural France and in the south-eastern areas of West Germany. But throughout much of Western Europe the village wholly engaged or serving agriculture has become—or is becoming—the exception to the general rule of suburbanization.

It is this unrural element which is responsible, directly and indirectly, for the legislation and the other action which most countries now think necessary to 'preserve' the countryside. This is a wholly new phenomenon in modern times in Britain. Previous attempts to maintain the *status quo* were aimed at the structure of farming itself: the Tudors and their Commonweal men legislated to keep the land under the plough, for 'shepherds be ill archers'. Thereafter, a few lone and ineffective voices were raised against enclosure or in favour of three acres and a cow. Structural legislation of this sort is now used in Denmark, Holland and Switzerland to prevent the amalgamation of farms from denuding their countrysides of their peasant elements; while Britain, France and Germany are using State powers to encourage amalgamation. But non-agricultural matters were left to pursue their natural courses till town and country planning acts, county by-laws, national park and nature conservancy commissions, orders for the prohibition of organochlorine pesticides began to proliferate because it was thought that the controls of the national economy were no longer sufficient protection. Most

of these measures have been as much defensive against agriculture as defending it; they are designed partly to protect the
townsman's interests in the rural Britain that urbanism and
suburbanism are threatening to destroy by indiscriminate housebuilding and modern agriculture is succeeding in changing by
the removal of hedgerows, and the consequent loss of hedge-
nesting birds, the spraying out of existence of predators and the
rarer flora, the silent acquisition of disused commonland, the
quiet closure of little-frequented footpaths. The dichotomy of
interests is most marked in the highly industrialized and thickly
populated nations of Britain and West Germany, less acute in
Holland and Denmark where ancient traditions of urban and
rural neighbourliness and mutual concern still hold, and scarcely
existing in France where the countryman remains the key figure
in the national community.

The acceleration of the rate of change in farming is now so
great that the shape of future developments, even a few decades
ahead, is not easy to see. In Britain the rise in population and
its demand for *lebensraum* make necessary demands upon agricultural land which are not likely to lessen until building proceeds
vertically and not horizontally, in some such form as the plan
to erect a two-mile high dwelling for 500,000 people on a four-
acre site in order to save a hundred square miles of countryside
from 'development'. On what land remains in farm use the pattern
of both social organization and food production seems likely to
change fast. The days of the independent farmer may be numbered. After all, like the farm horse whose loss seems equally
deplorable to many people, he emerged only recently—historically speaking—from the amalgam of mediaeval communal agriculture. Problems of supply, scale of production, marketing, the
provision of finance, co-operation in specialized techniques may
all find a solution in the joint stock farming company scarcely
distinguishable from the industrial firm except that it deals in
animals and plants, not chemicals and cars. Internationalism
may induce greater, even national, specialization in production
as American beef calves from the prairies are flown to southern
Europe to be reared and fattened on Italian and French maize
and Scandinavia breeds the pigs for British barley to turn into

bacon—all factory processes carried out in rural factory premises. The farm worker may become purely an agricultural technician in a white coat or blue boiler-suit; the farmer mainly a skilful deployer of capital into profitable channels; the village a dormitory or home for the affluent aged, squatting on the countryside, but not of it; the hills a vast week-end play park; the lowlands a great arable field dotted with meat, milk and egg production units that have lost all resemblance to the Norfolk crewyard, the Somerset cowshippen, the universal cottage pigsty and henhouse.

The business of growing food for human sustenance has come a long way in the ten thousand years since men ceased to be merely hunters and food gatherers. It will go a very much further way yet, to points beyond present imagining.

BOOKS FOR FURTHER READING

This book began as an attempt to establish the foreign influences which had contributed to the development of British agriculture and rural life. It soon became apparent that this called for a wide-ranging survey of the farming of Western Europe, and beyond; and that the result would be more nearly an international agrarian history than had at first been intended. None the less, this book remains a freehand chart of the main evolutionary stream of Western European ideas and practices, rather than a finely detailed map with all the backwaters drawn in.

This, together with the dislike of the apparatus of footnotes and full bibliography which I believe the ordinary reader shares with me, has supported me in my inclination to omit both. The sources are sufficiently familiar to the agricultural historian. Any reader who wants to pursue particular points will find the references easily enough in one or other of the following readily accessible books, to the authors of whom I am indebted for the involuntary loan (and occasional repayment) of many facts.

CLARK, J. G. D. *Prehistoric Europe*. London, 1952.

RIVET, A. L. F. *Town and Country in Roman Britain*. London, 1958.

BATH, B. H. SLICHER VAN. *Agrarian History of Western Europe A.D. 500–1850*. London, 1963.

ERNLE, LORD. *English Farming Past and Present* (6th edition), London, 1962 (with detailed bibliographical introductions by G. E. Fussell and O. R. McGregor).

TROW-SMITH, ROBERT. *History of British Livestock Husbandry to 1700*. London, 1957; *History of British Livestock Husbandry 1700–1900*. London, 1959.

FUSSELL, G. E. *The Farmer's Tools 1500–1900*. London, 1952.

ORWIN, C. S. AND WHETHAM, E. H. *History of British Agriculture 1846–1914*. London, 1964.

TRACY, MICHAEL. *Agriculture in Western Europe: Crisis and Adaptation since 1880.* London, 1964

CLAPHAM, J. H. AND POWER, E. (ed.). *Cambridge Economic History of Europe*, I, Cambridge, 1942 (especially Koebner, R., *Settlement and Colonization*; Stevens, C. E., *Agriculture and Rural Life in the Later Roman Empire*; Parain, C., *Evolution of Agricultural Technique*; and Bloch, M., *Rise of Dependent Cultivation and Seigniorial Institutions*).

Index

Index

Aalst, 96

Abergwessin (Brecon), 112

Adulteration of Food Act (1872), 168

Agrardemagogie in Deutschland, 162

Agricultural Research Council, 213

Agriculture Act (1947), 207

Algemene Nederlandse Zuivelbond, 164

Alps, deserted villages, 76

Alrum (Jutland), 33

Alsace, 65, 142

Althorpe, Lord, 138

Amoroso, E. C., 174

Anderson, Thos., 196

Annals of Agriculture, 131, 150

Ardennes, 108

artificial insemination, 218

Artois, 142

Austria, 98

Avon (Wiltshire), 30

Backhaus, A., 142

Bakewell, Robert, 129 *ff.*

Bakker, D. L., 172

Baldock (Herts.), 77, 199

Baldwin V., 64

Ballacagan (Isle of Man), 44

Banbury (Oxon.), 167

Bangham, 171

Barbegan (Arles), 38

Barclay of Ure, 138

barley, origin, 12; prehistoric, 29

Barkaer (Denmark), 43

Basel, 25

Bates, Thomas, 137

Bath and West Society, 150

Bath, S. van, 55, 107, 143

Bavaria, 69, 142, 181, 186

bean, Celtic, 35

beet, sugar, 145, 192

Bellerby, J. R., 156

Bennett, Harold, 198

Bennett, M. K., 93

Bernstorff, Count, 163

Biffin, Rowland, 191

binder, 197

Blyth, Walter, 106

Board of Agriculture, 130, 149

Böhure, O., 142

Bolton (Lancs.), 74

Booth, Thomas, 137

Bordeaux, 42

Bos longifrons, 20, 40, 113

Bos primigenius, 19–21, 29, 40, 113, 171

Boscombe Down (Wilts.), 34

Bourne, George, 95

Boutflour, Robert, 180

Brabant, 141

Bradfield Grange (Herts.), 80

Bradley, Richard, 110

Braunton (Devon), 54

Brecon (Wales), sheep milking, 60

Brendon (Somerset), 61

Brie, 78

Bronze Age, 30 *ff.*

Buckfast, abbey of, 80

Bund der Landwirte, 161

Bürger, C., 162

231

markets, medieval, 78; 19 cent., 167
Marlborough (Wilts.), 87
marling, 66
Marne valley, 42
Marsh Chapel (Lincs.), 76
Marshall, William, 110 ff., 129
McMeekan, Prof., 220
Meare (Somerset), 35
mechanization, 146 ff., 197 ff., 214-15
Mendip hills (Somerset), 73, 85
Meuse, 36
milk yield, 112, 137, 167, 173
milking machines, 174-5
mills, water, 38
Ministry of Agriculture, 206
Möckern Institute, 176
Möglin Institute, 176
monasteries, dissolution, 102. See also Cistercian, granges
Mörkeberg, Konsulent, 189
Mortimer, R., 111
Moryson, Fynes, 174
Moselle, 36
Mycenaeans, 30

National Agricultural Advisory Service, 213
National Farmers' Union, 159, 207
Nene valley, 37
Neolithic farming, 29 ff.
Netherlands, 98, 107, 120, 126, 141, 152, 164, 206
New Horse-Hoeing Husbandry, 110
Noëttes, L. des, 70
Nor (Norfolk), 37
Norfolk, 85, 142, 145
Northern Forest culture, 30
Norwich, 167
nutrition, animal, 175

oats, origin, 13; wild, 35
oilcake, 111, 177-9
Ouse (Cambs.), 37

Paris International Salon, 141, 186
parish administration, 122
Parkes, Josiah, 198
Peel, Sir Robert, 155
Pig Industry Development Authority, 218
pig (Sus scrofa), origin, 21; Neolithic, 29; Roman, 41; medieval, 58; 18 cent., 116; 19 cent., 187, 190; 20 cent., 217, 220
pig, Bayeux, 190
Berkshire, 116, 190
Boulonnais, 190
Chinese (Sus indicus), 21, 116, 188
Danish Landrace, 189
Edelschwein, 190
Goleb, 190
Landrace, 189
Large White, 189, 220
Leicestershire, 116
Lincolnshire Curlycoat, 189
Mangalista, 189
Neapolitan, 21, 188
Normandy, 190
Tigerschwein, 190
Veredeltes Landschwein, 190
Welsh, 116
Pisani, M., 209
place-names, 57, 76
plough, origin, 14; prehistoric, 31, 33; Roman, 40; medieval, 68; 16 cent., 94; 18 cent., 147
Po valley, 216
Pontefract (Yorks.), 74
Poor Laws, 123